KIM MARSHALL

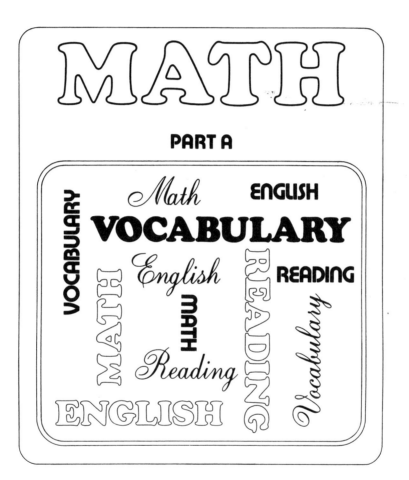

MATH

PART A

VOCABULARY

Math ENGLISH

VOCABULARY

English READING

MATH READING

Reading

ENGLISH Vocabulary

Educators Publishing Service, Inc.

31 Smith Place, Cambridge, MA 02138-1000

Acknowledgments

Without the frank comments of my students in the Martin Luther King School in Boston, this book would not be what it is today. They gave me new insights every day, and they deserve much credit for the sequence, organization, content, and breakdown of the units in the book.

Rudd Crawford, a fellow teacher of math, is responsible for the idea of the cumulative review process, which he developed in a somewhat different form in his classroom in Brookline, Massachusetts. He is also responsible for Unit 9 on Adding and Subtracting Decimals. I am grateful to him, Mary Scott, and Ransom Lynch for their ideas, encouragement, and criticism over the years.

Jeff Rubin, an editor from Educators Publishing Service, played a major role in resequencing the units, eliminating unnecessary sections, revising the review pages, and expanding and rewriting the measurement units. His ideas have greatly improved the book.

I am grateful to these and other people for their substantive contributions, and to my wife, Rhoda Schneider, for her invaluable support over the last ten years.

April, 1997 Printing

Contents

To the Student

Math is divided into *Part A* and *Part B* and includes a total of thirty-five units. This book is *Part A*. The two books cover basic skills, Roman numerals, measurement, graphing, fractions, and basic geometry. If you work carefully through each unit, you should become a better math student and should be more confident in your ability to use math outside of school.

Each unit introduces one new skill. The sequence within each unit progresses as follows:

Page one and page two teach the new material.

Page three is a review with short practice questions on all the skills learned in previous units, so you won't forget them.

Page four and page five provide more practice on new material.

Page six is a test on the material learned in that unit.

Page seven (beginning in Unit 4) is a Review Test that has one exercise covering each skill introduced up to that point in the book.

The two-part box at the top of each page is for your grade. The number already filled in is the number of questions on that page; the empty part of the box is for you or your teacher to write in the number you got right. At the back of the book is a progress chart where you can keep track of your grades on Unit Tests and on Review Tests. There is also a special bar graph on which to record your grades on these Review Tests. The top line of the bar graph indicates the level of one hundred percent correct on these Review Tests. The lower line represents an eighty percent level of achievement. You should try to keep your bar graph above the eighty percent line.

Good luck with these books. I hope you find them interesting and helpful.

KIM MARSHALL

Figure out the *interval* (gap) between the numbers, and on the line fill in the number that comes next.

1. 2, 4, 6, _8_

2. 6, 9, 12, _15_

3. 12, 14, 16, _18_

4. 21, 22, 23, _24_

5. 7, 14, 21, _28_

6. 15, 18, 21, _24_

7. 10, 15, 20, _25_

8. 30, 40, 50, _60_

9. 24, 32, 40, _48_

10. 46, 48, 50, _52_

11. 33, 36, 39, _42_

Work the same way to fill in the following missing numbers.

12. 21, 24, _26_, 30, 33

13. 14, _21_, 28, 35

14. 40, _50_, _60_, 70, 80

15. 8, _10_, _12_, 14, 16

16. 6, 9, _12_, _15_, 18

17. 25, _30_, _35_, 40, 45

18. 27, 36, _45_, _54_, 63

19. 18, _20_, _22_, 24, 26

20. 11, 22, _33_, _44_, 55

Figure out the interval, and then fill in the gaps on each of the following number lines.

21. 12 | 15 | 18 | 21 | 24 | 27 | 30 33 | 36 39 42 | | 45 |

22. 10 | 15 | 20 25 | 30 35 40 45 50 | 55 | 60 65 70 75 |

Intervals 2

Fill in the missing numbers by figuring out the intervals.

1. 4, 8, 12, _____

2. 12, 14, 16, _____

3. 14, 21, 28, _____

4. 18, 27, 36, _____

5. 70, 80, 90, _____

6. 35, _____, 45, 50, _____

7. 22, _____, 44, 55, _____

8. 12, 18, _____, 30, _____

9. 15, _____, _____, 30, 35

10. 68, _____, _____, 74, _____

Figure out the intervals, and then fill in the gaps on the following number lines.

First find the interval, and then figure out what *A* should be on the following number line.

14. 8 ___|___|___|___|___|___ A ___|___|___|___ 26   A = _____

In each unit there will be a *Review* mixed in with the regular work pages. The *Review* is to give you a chance to practice all the things you've learned. This way you won't forget them.

Work out the answers to the following problems.

1.
$$\begin{array}{r} 85 \\ \times\ 6 \\ \hline \end{array}$$

2.
$$\begin{array}{r} 73 \\ \times\ 5 \\ \hline \end{array}$$

3.
$$\begin{array}{r} 96 \\ \times\ 4 \\ \hline \end{array}$$

4.
$$\begin{array}{r} 94 \\ \times\ 8 \\ \hline \end{array}$$

5.
$$\begin{array}{r} 297 \\ \times\ 4 \\ \hline \end{array}$$

6.
$$\begin{array}{r} 478 \\ \times\ 8 \\ \hline \end{array}$$

7.
$$\begin{array}{r} 942 \\ -\ 137 \\ \hline \end{array}$$

8.
$$\begin{array}{r} 264 \\ -\ 128 \\ \hline \end{array}$$

9.
$$\begin{array}{r} 9471 \\ -\ 215 \\ \hline \end{array}$$

10.
$$\begin{array}{r} 7742 \\ -\ 418 \\ \hline \end{array}$$

11.
$$\begin{array}{r} 9266 \\ -\ 149 \\ \hline \end{array}$$

12.
$$\begin{array}{r} 77892 \\ +\ 21773 \\ \hline \end{array}$$

13.
$$\begin{array}{r} 4593 \\ 6845 \\ +\ 2180 \\ \hline \end{array}$$

14.
$$\begin{array}{r} 7491 \\ 2811 \\ 4952 \\ +\ 2371 \\ \hline \end{array}$$

15.
$$\begin{array}{r} 88 \\ 35 \\ 92 \\ 74 \\ 35 \\ +\ 68 \\ \hline \end{array}$$

Figure out the intervals, and fill in the gaps on the following number lines.

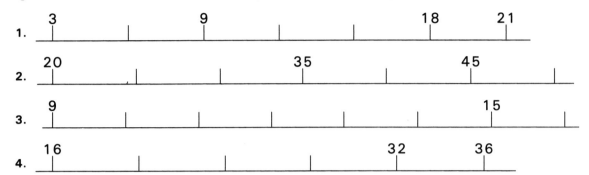

1. 3   9   18   21

2. 20   35   45

3. 9   15

4. 16   32   36

Find the interval, and then figure out what *A* should be on each of the following number lines.

5. 10   A   26   A = _____

6. 32   A   64   A = _____

7. 30   A   70   A = _____

8. 90   A   102   A = _____

Intervals 4

Fill in the missing numbers by figuring out the intervals.

1. 24, _____, _____, 33, 36

2. 0, 6, _____, _____, _____

3. 7, _____, 21, 28, _____

4. _____, 44, 46, 48, _____

5. 8, 16, _____, _____, _____

6. 30, _____, 40, _____, 50

7. _____, 7, 14, _____, _____

8. 14, 16, _____, _____, _____

9. 10, _____, _____, _____, 50

10. 5, _____, _____, 20, 25

Figure out the intervals, and then fill in the gaps on the following number lines.

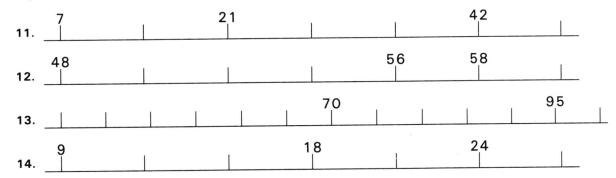

11. 7   21   42

12. 48   56   58

13.   70   95

14. 9   18   24

First find the interval, and then figure out what _A_ should be on each of the following number lines.

15. 14   20   A   A = _____

16.   40   50   A   A = _____

17. 12   A   33   A = _____

Find the interval, and then figure out what *A* should be on each of the following number lines.

1. 6   A   14   A = _____

2. 20   A   40   A = _____

3. 7   A   13   A = _____

4. 30   A   80   A = _____

5. 35   A   70   A = _____

6. 12   A   36   A = _____

7. 8   A   40   A = _____

8. 16   A   40   A = _____

9. 200   A   600   A = _____

10. 30   A   48   A = _____

Fill in this *times table chart*. Try to make it perfect — no mistakes! Start with 0 × 0. You may wish to refer back to this grid as you go through this book.

X	0	1	2	3	4	5	6	7	8	9	10	11	12
0													
1													
2													
3													
4													
5													
6													
7													
8													
9													
10													
11													
12													

On the line, write each number in words. The spellings are given below. Use a dash between a number ending in *ty* and another number, for example: *thirty-four, fifty-nine.*

1	one	5	five	9	nine	13	thirteen	17	seventeen	30	thirty	70	seventy
2	two	6	six	10	ten	14	fourteen	18	eighteen	40	forty	80	eighty
3	three	7	seven	11	eleven	15	fifteen	19	nineteen	50	fifty	90	ninety
4	four	8	eight	12	twelve	16	sixteen	20	twenty	60	sixty	100	one hundred

1. 27 _____

2. 49 _____

3. 81 _____

4. 98 _____

5. 53 _____

6. 211 _____

7. 318 _____

8. 104 _____

9. 622 _____

10. 914 _____

11. 299 _____

12. 325 _____

13. 788 _____

14. 313 _____

15. 470 _____

16. 901 _____

Write the following words as numbers.

17. five hundred sixty-two _____

18. four hundred ninety-eight _____

19. two hundred fourteen _____

20. four hundred twelve _____

21. six hundred two _____

22. seven hundred eighty-six _____

Writing Numbers as Words 2

Write the following numbers as words. Spellings are given below.

2 two	12 twelve	18 eighteen	80 eighty
4 four	13 thirteen	40 forty	90 ninety
8 eight	14 fourteen	50 fifty	100 one hundred
11 eleven			

1. 355 _____

2. 299 _____

3. 146 _____

4. 864 _____

5. 349 _____

6. 999 _____

7. 540 _____

8. 504 _____

9. 450 _____

10. 111 _____

11. 302 _____

12. 805 _____

Write the following words as numbers.

13. seven hundred twenty-five _____

14. nine hundred thirty-six _____

15. four hundred one _____

16. three hundred sixty-six _____

17. five hundred seventy-two _____

18. nine hundred nine _____

19. nine hundred nineteen _____

20. four hundred twelve _____

Now work out this problem, and write the answer in words.

21. A woman will make twenty-nine dollars
    today and thirty-two dollars tomorrow.
    How much will she make in all?

    _____

Review 2

Find the interval, and then figure out what _A_ should be on each of the following number lines.

1.
```
15          A          25
|_____|_____|
```

A = _____

2.
```
12              A       21
|_____|_____|_____|
```

A = _____

3.
```
20   A                  40
|____|____|____|____|____|
```

A = _____

4.
```
25                 A    50
|____|____|____|____|____|
```

A = _____

5.
```
17                A     27
|__|__|__|__|__|__|__|__|__|
```

A = _____

6. (8 × 4) + (7 × 7) + (9 × 7) = _____

7. (6 × 9) + (8 × 6) + (7 × 6) = _____

8. (4 × 5) + (12 × 4) + (3 × 9) = _____

9. (19 × 2) + _____ = 100

10. (13 × 4) + _____ = 100

11. (15 × 5) + _____ = 100

12.
```
  742
×   7
```

13.
```
  925
×   6
```

14.
```
  218
×   4
```

15.
```
 7931
− 217
```

16.
```
 9403
− 812
```

17.
```
 2847
− 218
```

18.
```
  3794
  4489
+ 2208
```

19.
```
  7743
  2891
  7726
+ 4091
```

10

Write the following numbers as words.

1. 895 _____

2. 123 _____

3. 579 _____

4. 996 _____

5. 885 _____

6. 213 _____

7. 317 _____

8. 818 _____

9. 793 _____

10. 203 _____

11. 709 _____

Now write the following words as numbers.

12. seven hundred fifty-nine _____

13. two hundred thirteen _____

14. five hundred eighteen _____

15. five hundred eighty _____

16. five hundred eight _____

17. nine hundred one _____

18. one hundred nineteen _____

19. six hundred forty-two _____

20. six hundred six _____

21. eight hundred fifty-nine _____

22. four hundred eighty-eight _____

23. two hundred _____

24. six hundred thirteen _____

25. two hundred twelve _____

26. three hundred nineteen _____

27. two hundred ninety _____

Work out the following problem, and write the answer in words.

28. A boy paid one hundred thirty-five dollars
for a tent and one hundred thirteen dollars
for a bicycle. How much did he spend
in all?

_____

Write the following numbers as words.

1. 398 _____

2. 202 _____

3. 403 _____

4. 514 _____

5. 980 _____

6. 616 _____

7. 392 _____

8. 912 _____

9. 206 _____

10. 365 _____

11. 414 _____

12. 441 _____

Write the following words as numbers.

13. three hundred thirteen _____

14. three hundred thirty-one _____

15. three hundred thirty _____

16. five hundred one _____

17. two hundred eighty-six _____

18. six hundred sixteen _____

19. seven hundred sixty-one _____

20. two hundred sixty-nine _____

21. nine hundred twenty-six _____

22. six hundred twenty-nine _____

23. six hundred ninety-two _____

24. two hundred seventeen _____

25. eight hundred eighteen _____

26. five hundred five _____

Now work out the following two problems, and write the answers in words.

27. A girl worked part time and made thirty-seven dollars one week, twenty-nine dollars the next, and forty-eight dollars the week after that. How much did she make in all?

_____

28. There were three hundred eighty-six girls in a school and four hundred twelve boys. How many students were in the school?

_____

Write the following numbers as words.

1. 246 _____

2. 415 _____

3. 290 _____

4. 386 _____

5. 891 _____

6. 355 _____

7. 801 _____

8. 212 _____

9. 513 _____

10. 890 _____

11. 706 _____

12. 614 _____

Write the following words as numbers.

13. three hundred seventy-nine _____

14. two hundred eighty _____

15. nine hundred nineteen _____

16. seven hundred twenty-four _____

17. three hundred seventeen _____

18. six hundred forty-one _____

19. two hundred fourteen _____

Now solve the following problem, and write the answer in words.

20. Ming makes one hundred seventy-three
dollars a week. How much can she make in
four weeks?

_____

Carefully solve the following problems.

1. 781
    489
    + 743

2. 6493
    2891
    + 4083

3. 9874
    2281
    4836
    + 2890

4. 7736
    − 2291

5. 6942
    − 1469

6. 12741
    − 9623

7. 649
    ×   3

8. 4361
    ×   5

9. 2986
    ×   8

Find the interval, and then figure out what _A_ should be on each of the following number lines.

10. 15 ———————— A ———————— 40   A = _____

11. 12 ———————— A ———————— 27   A = _____

12. 21 ———— A ———————— 63   A = _____

The *factors* of a number are the numbers that divide evenly into it.
The factors of 6 are **2** and **3** because 2 × 3 = 6.

Write the factors of each of the following numbers. (Don't count the number itself or 1.)

1. The factors of 4 are _____ × _____.

2. The factors of 6 are _____ × _____.

3. The factors of 8 are _____ × _____.

4. The factors of 9 are _____ × _____.

5. The factors of 10 are _____ × _____.

6. The factors of 14 are _____ × _____.

7. The factors of 15 are _____ × _____.

8. The factors of 21 are _____ × _____.

9. The factors of 22 are _____ × _____.

10. The factors of 25 are _____ × _____.

11. The factors of 26 are _____ × _____.

12. The factors of 27 are _____ × _____.

13. The factors of 33 are _____ × _____.

The following numbers have more than one set of factors. See if you can think of all of them. (Don't count the number itself or 1.)

14. The factors of 12 are _____ × _____   also _____ × _____.

15. The factors of 16 are _____ × _____   also _____ × _____.

16. The factors of 18 are _____ × _____   also _____ × _____.

17. The factors of 20 are _____ × _____   also _____ × _____.

18. The factors of 24 are _____ × _____   also _____ × _____   also _____ × _____.

19. The factors of 28 are _____ × _____   also _____ × _____ .

20. The factors of 30 are _____ × _____   also _____ × _____   also _____ × _____.

Factors and Prime Numbers 2

A number that has only two factors, 1 and the number itself, is called a *prime number*. The number 1 is an exception; it is not considered prime.

Write the factors of the following numbers. The numbers with an asterisk (*) by them have more than one set of factors. If a number doesn't have any factors other than one and itself, write *prime* on the line.

1. 4   2 × 2   18. 21 _____

2. 5   prime   19. 22 _____

3. 6 _____   20. 23 _____

4. 7 _____   21. 24* _____

5. 8 _____   22. 25 _____

6. 9 _____   23. 26 _____

7. 10 _____   24. 27 _____

8. 11 _____   25. 28* _____

9. 12* _____   26. 29 _____

10. 13 _____   27. 30* _____

11. 14 _____   28. 31 _____

12. 15 _____   29. 32* _____

13. 16* _____   30. 33 _____

14. 17 _____   31. 34 _____

15. 18* _____   32. 35 _____

16. 19 _____   33. 36* _____

17. 20* _____

Review 3

Find the interval, and then figure out what _A_ should be on each of the following number lines.

1.
```
15        A              20
|____|____|____|____|____|
```

A = _____

2.
```
20              A         70
|____|____|____|____|____|
```

A = _____

3.
```
18   A                    63
|____|____|____|____|____|
```

A = _____

4.
```
24         A         40
|_____|_____|_____|
```

A = _____

5.
```
22         A    55
|_____|_____|_____|
```

A = _____

Write the following words as numbers.

6. five hundred twenty-three _____

7. two hundred two_____

8. eight hundred seventy _____

9. three hundred eleven _____

10. four hundred four _____

11. six hundred eight_____

Write the following numbers as words.

12. 693 _____

13. 314 _____

14. 297 _____

15. 880 _____
   _____

16. 112_____
   _____

17. 754 _____
   _____

18. $(4 \times 8) + (7 \times 3) + (9 \times 2)$ = _____

19. $(9 \times 8) + (6 \times 7) + (11 \times 3)$ = _____

20. $(4 \times 7) + (8 \times 7) + (4 \times 8)$ = _____

21. $(4 \times 8) +$ _____ $= 100$

22. $(6 \times 7) +$ _____ $= 100$

23. $(3 \times 12) +$ _____ $= 100$

24. The best tickets to a rock concert cost $15. How much would 9 of these tickets cost?

_____

25. A woman had several savings accounts in different banks. She had $4,890 in one bank, $7,000 in another, $9,048 in a third, and $4,299 in a fourth. How much money did she have in all 4 banks?

_____

26. A family began to drive across the United States, a drive of 2,893 miles. On the first day they covered 567 miles. How far did they have left to travel?

_____

27.
```
  4793
-  218
```

28.
```
  9301
-  140
```

29.
```
  7789
  2874
+ 3899
```

17

Write the factors of the following numbers. An asterisk (*) means that a number has more than one set of factors. Write *prime* by any number that doesn't have factors other than 1 and itself.

1. 2 _____

2. 4 _____

3. 6 _____

4. 8 _____

5. 10 _____

6. 12*_____

7. 14 _____

8. 16*_____

9. 18*_____

10. 20*_____

11. 21 _____

12. 23 _____

13. 24*_____

14. 25 _____

15. 26 _____

16. 28*_____

17. 30*_____

18. 32*_____

19. 34 _____

20. 36*_____

21. 37 _____

22. 38 _____

23. 40*_____

24. 42*_____

25. 43 _____

26. 44*_____

27. 45*_____

Write the factors of the following numbers. An asterisk (*) means that a number has more than one set of factors. Write *prime* by any number that doesn't have factors other than 1 and itself.

1. 3 _____

2. 5 _____

3. 7 _____

4. 8 _____

5. 9 _____

6. 10 _____

7. 2 _____

8. 4 _____

9. 6 _____

10. 11 _____

11. 13 _____

12. 21 _____

13. 23 _____

14. 24 * _____

15. 25 _____

16. 27 _____

17. 29 _____

18. 30 * _____

19. 31 _____

20. 33 _____

21. 35 _____

22. 36 * _____

23. 41 _____

24. 42 * _____

25. 43 _____

26. 45 * _____

27. 47 _____

28. 49 _____

29. 50 * _____

On the following lines, fill in the missing prime numbers.

30. 2, 3, _____, _____, 11, 13, _____,

_____, _____, 29, _____, _____, 41,

_____, 47, _____

Write the factors of the following numbers. An asterisk (*) means that a number has more than one set of factors.

Examples:
8 = 2 × 4
40 = 2 × 20, 4 × 10, 5 × 8

Write *prime* by any number that doesn't have factors other than 1 and itself.

1. 6 _____

2. 7 _____

3. 9 _____

4. 10 _____

5. 11 _____

6. 12 * _____

7. 14 _____

8. 15 _____

9. 16 * _____

10. 17 _____

11. 18 * _____

12. 20 * _____

13. 21 _____

14. 22 _____

15. 24 * _____

16. 25 _____

17. 26 _____

18. 27 _____

19. 28 * _____

20. 29 _____

21. 30 * _____

22. 31 _____

23. 32 * _____

Work out the following problems.

1.
```
  6492
  4307
+ 9984
```

2.
```
  4287
  7403
  9456
+ 2945
```

3.
```
  6389
- 2197
```

4.
```
  4036
- 1427
```

5.
```
  9427
×    7
```

6.
```
  6403
×    5
```

Find the interval, and then figure out what _A_ should be on each of the following number lines.

7.
```
24                          A        54
```
A = _____

8.
```
24                  A              64
```
A = _____

9.
```
24          A                    84
```
A = _____

Write the following numbers as words.

10. 749 _____

11. 218 _____

12. 604 _____

Write the following words as numbers.

13. six hundred eighteen _____

14. nine hundred two _____

15. five hundred seventy-four _____

Break down each number to its factors. (Don't use the number itself or 1.) Keep breaking numbers down to their factors until you get only prime numbers. Write the prime factors on the line below each problem.

Example:

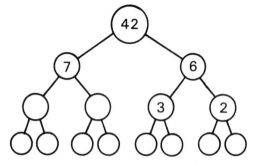

Prime factors of 42 = _____ 7 × 3 × 2 _____

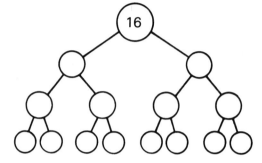

1. Prime factors of 16 = _____

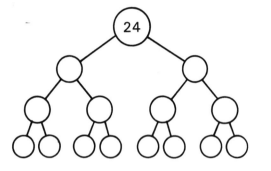

2. Prime factors = _____

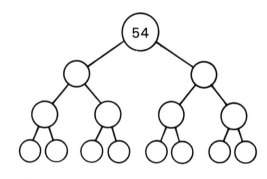

3. Prime factors = _____

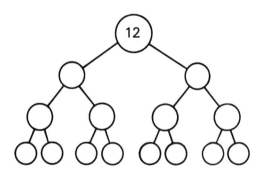

4. Prime factors = _____

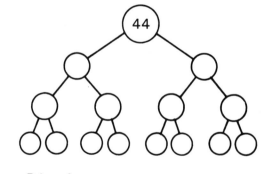

5. Prime factors = _____

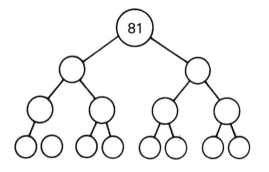

6. Prime factors = _____

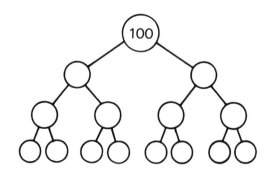

7. Prime factors = _____

Break down each number to its factors. Don't use the number itself or 1. Keep going until you get only prime factors. Then write the prime factors on the line below each problem.

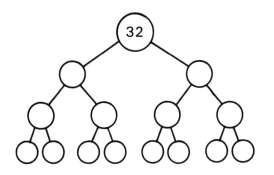

1. Prime factors = _____

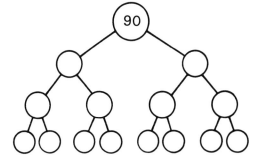

2. Prime factors = _____

Do the factors of 18 two ways. Will the factors be the same? _____

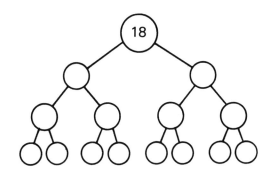

3. Prime factors = _____

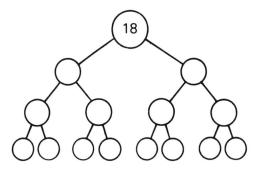

4. Prime factors = _____

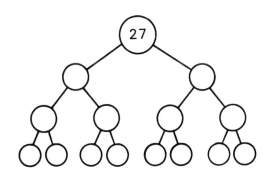

5. Prime factors = _____

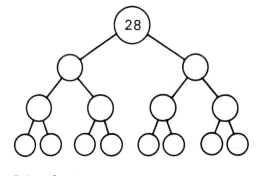

6. Prime factors = _____

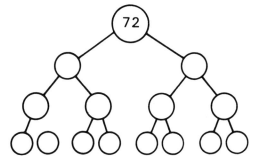

7. Prime factors = _____

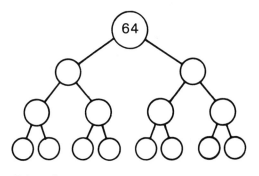

8. Prime factors = _____

Find the interval, and then figure out what A should be on each of the following number lines.

1.
```
18           A          28
 |___|___|___|___|___|
```

A = _____

2.
```
30        A           80
 |___|___|___|___|___|
```

A = _____

3.
```
20  A                 25
 |___|___|___|___|___|
```

A = _____

4.
```
16                A   56
 |___|___|___|___|___|
```

A = _____

Write the following numbers as words.

5. 348 _____
_____

6. 112 _____
_____

7. 217 _____
_____

8. 502 _____
_____

9. 888 _____
_____

10. 945 _____
_____

Write the following words as numbers.

11. three hundred forty-eight _____

12. five hundred ninety_____

13. four hundred nine _____

14. eight hundred fifty-seven _____

15. six hundred sixty-one_____

16. seven hundred _____

Write the factors of each of the following numbers. Some numbers may have more than one set of factors. Write *prime* by any number that doesn't have factors other than 1 and itself.

17. 28 _____   20. 21 _____

_____   21. 11 _____

18. 33 _____   22. 16 _____

19. 9 _____   _____

23. A man makes $35 a day. How much can he make working 6 days?

_____

24. A champion bricklayer can lay 684 bricks in 1 hour. How many bricks can he lay in 8 hours of work?

_____

25. Shawnna got $50 for her birthday from her grandmother. She spent $37 on a bracelet and $9 on an afternoon snack. How much of the money did she have left?

_____

26. $(9 \times 9) + (8 \times 8) + (7 \times 7) =$ _____

27. $(11 \times 8) +$ _____ $= 100$

28.
```
  6831
-  414
```

30.
```
  7894
  2731
  2899
+  403
```

29.
```
  1201
-  420
```

Break down each number to its prime factors. Then write these factors on the line below each problem.

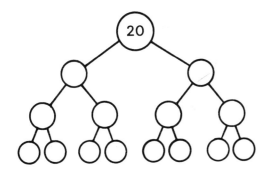

1. Prime factors = _____

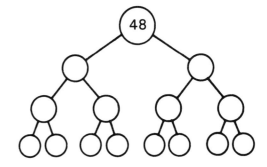

2. Prime factors = _____

Do the factors of 36 two ways.

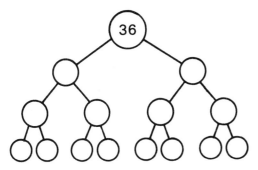

3. Prime factors = _____

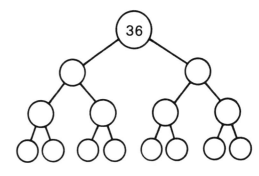

4. Prime factors = _____

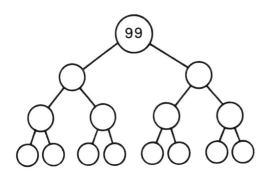

5. Prime factors = _____

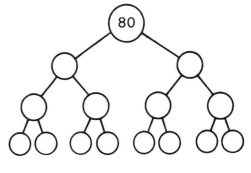

6. Prime factors = _____

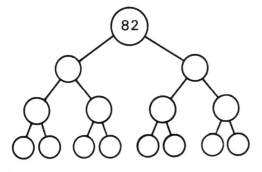

7. Prime factors = _____

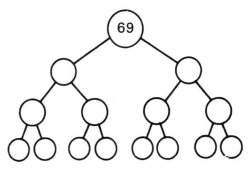

8. Prime factors = _____

Break down each number to its prime factors. Write these factors on the line below each problem.

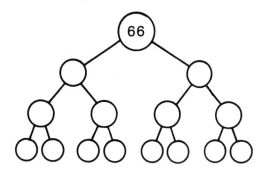

1. Prime factors = _____

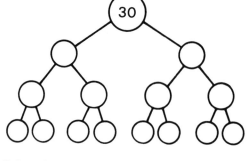

2. Prime factors = _____

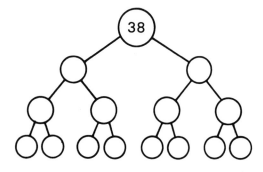

3. Prime factors = _____

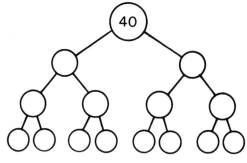

4. Prime factors = _____

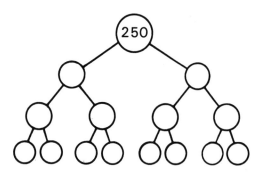

5. Prime factors = _____

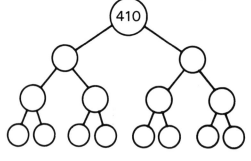

6. Prime factors = _____

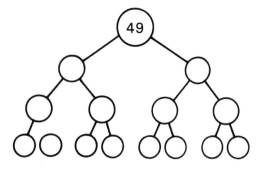

7. Prime factors = _____

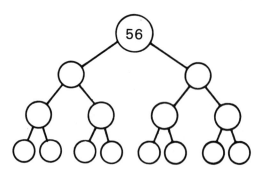

8. Prime factors = _____

Break down each number to its prime factors. Write these factors on the line below each problem.

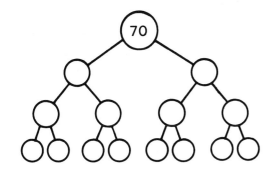

1. Prime factors = _____

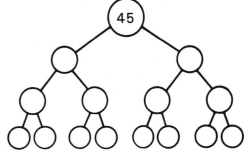

2. Prime factors = _____

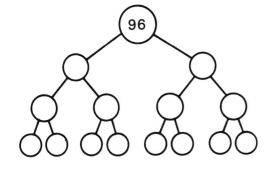

3. Prime factors = _____

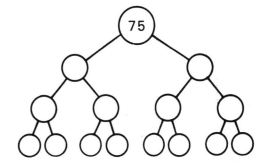

4. Prime factors = _____

This is the first of the Review Tests that you will take at the end of each week. The tests will go over the skills you have learned in previous weeks. The idea is to test you on new skills as you learn them and also to give you practice with the old ones. This way, by the end of the year, you should be good at the skills you've learned and practiced in this book.

Each skill will always be the same question number; for instance, question two will always be on writing numbers as words. As the tests get longer during the year, you will find the questions at the beginning easier and easier because you will have practiced them so much. If you do get a question wrong, be sure to check it over and understand your mistake. That way you will get it right on the next test you take.

1. Find the interval, and then figure out what *A* is on each of the following number lines.

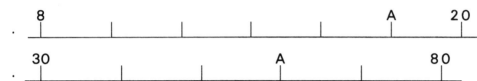

A = _____

A = _____

2. Write 308 using words. _____

   Write six hundred forty-nine using numbers. _____

3. Factor 20 two ways. _____   _____

   Factor 18 two ways. _____   _____

Unit 5—One-Number Division 1

When you divide, follow the four steps below.

1) Divide	2) Multiply	3) Subtract	4) Bring down

$$
\begin{array}{r} 3 \\ 5\overline{)185} \end{array}
\qquad
\begin{array}{r} 3 \\ 5\overline{)185} \\ 15 \end{array}
\qquad
\begin{array}{r} 3 \\ 5\overline{)185} \\ -15 \\ \hline 3 \end{array}
\qquad
\begin{array}{r} 3 \\ 5\overline{)185} \\ -15\downarrow \\ \hline 35 \end{array}
$$

Continue to follow these four steps until all the numbers are used up.

1) Divide	2) Multiply	3) Subtract

$$
\begin{array}{r} 37 \\ 5\overline{)185} \\ 15 \\ \hline 35 \end{array}
\qquad
\begin{array}{r} 37 \\ 5\overline{)185} \\ 15 \\ \hline 35 \\ 35 \end{array}
\qquad
\begin{array}{r} 37 \\ 5\overline{)185} \\ 15 \\ \hline 35 \\ -35 \\ \hline 0 \end{array}
$$

Follow the four steps used in division to solve the following problems.

1. $7\overline{)413}$

2. $4\overline{)252}$

3. $9\overline{)4716}$

4. $6\overline{)444}$

5. $5\overline{)3410}$

6. $3\overline{)171}$

7. $4\overline{)3352}$

29

One-Number Division 2

Solve the following division problems. Divide carefully.
Remember the four steps:
1) Divide
2) Multiply
3) Subtract
4) Bring down

Example:

```
      793
3 ) 2379
   -21
    27
   -27
    09
    -9
     0
```

1.
```
5 ) 9860
```

2.
```
7 ) 3689
```

3.
```
6 ) 1686
```

4.
```
4 ) 10288
```

5.
```
9 ) 47466
```

6.
```
4 ) 3304
```

7.
```
5 ) 9380
```

Solve the following problems by applying the four steps used in division. Put your answer on the line below each problem.

8. Carlos drives 3,204 miles in 6 days. On average, how far did he drive each day?

_____

9. Karen won $1,575. She decided to divide the money evenly among herself and her 6 children. (That's 7 people.) How much did each person get?

_____

10. A man paid $3,249 for a used car. He paid for the car in 9 equal payments. How much was each payment?

_____

Review 5

Find the interval, and then figure out what *A* should be on each of the following number lines.

1.
```
14              A              49
|___|___|___|___|___|___|
```
A = _____

2.
```
24                    A    54
|___|___|___|___|___|___|
```
A = _____

3.
```
13   A                      18
|___|___|___|___|___|___|
```
A = _____

4.
```
18        A                 63
|___|___|___|___|___|___|
```
A = _____

Write the following words as numbers.

5. five hundred eighty-five _____

6. nine hundred twelve _____

7. four hundred fifty _____

8. six hundred one _____

9. one hundred two _____

Write the following numbers as words.

10. 402 _____
_____

11. 297 _____
_____

12. 444 _____
_____

13. 314 _____
_____

14. 910 _____
_____

Write the factors of the numbers below. Some numbers may have more than one set of factors. Write *prime* if a number has no factors other than 1 and itself.

15. 6_____   18. 18_____

16. 22_____   19. 19_____

17. 34_____   20. 45_____

21. George drove at 56 miles an hour. How far did he go in 4 hours?

_____

22. $(9 \times 6) + (12 \times 4) + (8 \times 3) =$ _____

23. $(21 \times 4) +$ _____ $= 100$

24.
```
  5783
-  269
```

25.
```
  1630
-  247
```

26.
```
  8951
×    4
```

27.
```
  1773
-  591
```

28.
```
  3000
-  264
```

29.
```
   847
   291
   609
+  214
```

30.
```
  7900
-  216
```

31

Apply the four steps used in division to solve the following problems. These problems will have remainders. Write these remainders as fractions (remainder on top, divisor on bottom).

Example:
$$7)\overline{2589} = 369\tfrac{6}{7}$$
```
      369 6/7
7 ) 2589
    21
    48
    42
    69
    63
     6
```

1.
```
4 ) 3507
```

2.
```
3 ) 4831
```

3.
```
8 ) 6621
```

Follow the four steps used in division in the next four problems. These problems have a zero (0) in the middle of the answer. Be sure to put it in!

Example:
```
    804
6 ) 4824
    48
    02
    00
    24
    24
     0
```

4.
```
9 ) 954
```

5.
```
7 ) 6314
```

6.
```
3 ) 25512
```

Solve the following problems. Put your answer on the line below each problem.

7. A teacher makes $5, 196 in 6 weeks. How much does he make each week?

   _____

8. Three brothers inherit $15,201. They decide to split the money evenly among themselves. How much does each brother get?

   _____

9. A high-speed train travels 1,134 miles in 9 hours. How far does it travel each hour?

   _____

Apply the four steps used in division to solve the following problems. Beware of zeroes in the answers!

1.
$$8 \overline{)9448}$$

2.
$$6 \overline{)36144}$$

3.
$$5 \overline{)4460}$$

4.
$$9 \overline{)32409}$$

Follow the four steps used in division in the next four problems. If there is a remainder, write it as a fraction (remainder on top, divisor on bottom).

5.
$$8 \overline{)5376}$$

6.
$$7 \overline{)2499}$$

7.
$$5 \overline{)8505}$$

8.
$$4 \overline{)14564}$$

Solve the following problems. Put your answer on the line below each problem.

9. Jamal worked for 9 months and made $5,103. How much did he make each month?

_____

10. A man wins $20,192 in the lottery. If he divides it among his 4 children, how much will each child get?

_____

11. Rosalinda wants to split $4,959 among 6 people. It won't go evenly. How much money is left over?

_____

Apply the four steps used in division to solve the following problems. Two of the problems have remainders. Be sure to write these remainders correctly.

1.
4) 2512

2.
5) 3594

3.
9) 7668

4.
7) 42357

5.
6) 37824

6.
3) 2344

7.
8) 3944

8.
7) 8911

Solve the next two problems. Put your answer on the line below each problem.

9. A jet traveled 4,564 miles in 7 hours.
   How far did it travel each hour?

   _____

10. Maria worked for 6 weeks and made
    $5,058. How much did she make each
    week?

    _____

1. Find the interval, and then figure out what *A* is on each of the following number lines.

A = _____

A = _____

2. Write 638 using words. _____

   Write three hundred fifty-seven using numbers. _____

3. Factor 24 three ways. _____ _____ _____

   Factor 16 two ways. _____ _____

To find the *average* of a set of numbers, follow these two steps:
 1) Add up all the numbers.
 2) Divide the sum by how many numbers there are.

Example:
 Find the average of 3, 7, and 11.

$$\begin{array}{r} 3 \\ 7 \\ + \ 11 \\ \hline 21 \end{array} \qquad \begin{array}{r} 7 \\ \overline{3 \,)\, 21} \end{array} \qquad \text{Answer} = \underline{\ \ 7 \ \ }$$

Solve the following problems.

1. Find the average of 5, 7, and 12. _____

2. Find the average of 6, 8, 10, 16, and 20. _____

3. Find the average of 148, 247, and 352. _____

4. Find the average of 5, 11, 15, and 17. _____

5. Find the average of 6, 9, 15, 18, 32, 40, and 90. _____

6. Find the average of 500 and 800. _____

7. A boy was playing a game and on ten tries made the following scores.
   First try—4
   Second try—6
   Third try—2
   Fourth try—12
   Fifth try—12
   Sixth try—12
   Seventh try—23
   Eighth try—22
   Ninth try—24
   Tenth try—43
   What was his average score for the
   ten tries?

   _____

Finding the Average 2

Remember to follow two steps to find an average:
1) Add up all the numbers.
2) Divide the sum by how many numbers there are.

Solve the following problems.

1. Find the average of 15, 33, 42, 78, and 102. _____

2. Find the average of 563 and 395. _____

3. Find the average of 4, 5, 8, 45, 66, and 70. _____

4. Find the average of 32, 43, and 51. _____

5. Below are the temperatures taken at six times during the day.

Dawn	41°F
9 A.M.	50°F
Noon	60°F
3 P.M.	75°F
6 P.M.	70°F
Midnight	40°F

   What was the average temperature of the day? _____

6. There are 3 people in a family. Here are their weights.

Papa	210 pounds
Mama	136 pounds
Junior	86 pounds

   What is the average weight of the people in the family? _____

Find the interval, and then figure out what _A_ should be on each of the following number lines.

1.
```
    14            A           24
    |---|---|---|---|---|---|
```

A = _____

2.
```
    15   A                   40
    |---|---|---|---|---|---|
```

A = _____

3.
```
    18                  A    48
    |---|---|---|---|---|---|
```

A = _____

Write the following numbers as words.

4. 908 _____

_____

5. 312 _____

_____

6. 594 _____

_____

7. 248 _____

_____

Write the following words as numbers.

8. three hundred fifty-nine _____

9. five hundred two _____

10. nine hundred eleven _____

11. four hundred ninety-six _____

Write the factors of each of the following numbers. Some numbers may have more than one set of factors. If a number is prime, write _prime_ on the line.

12. 4 _____ 13. 7 _____

14. 14 _____ 17. 12 _____

15. 25 _____ 18. 23 _____

16. 6 _____ 19. 33 _____

20. Factor 50 two ways. _____

_____

21. Factor 100 four ways. _____

_____

22. $(8 \times 7) +$ _____ $= 100$

23.
$$7\overline{)1813}$$

24.
$$9\overline{)7317}$$

25.
$$8\overline{)1344}$$

26. $6559 \div 6 =$ _____

27. $75310 \div 8 =$ _____

28. Bobby and 2 of his friends will take a bicycle trip through Vermont. They plan to travel about 45 miles each day. How far can they go in 9 days?

_____

29. How many cents could you get for 73 nickels?

_____

30. A jet travels 3,378 miles in 6 hours. How far is it traveling each hour?

_____

Solve the following problems.

1. Find the average of 8, 5, 4, 100, 3, 77, and 6. _____

2. Find the average of 23, 10, 2, 66, and 9. _____

3. Find the average of 15, 21, and 39. _____

4. Find the average of 100, 340, 800, and 80. _____

5. Find the average of 9, 4, 7, 2, 10, 11, and 6. _____

6. Find the average of 100 and 200. _____

7. During one week a girl made the following amounts of money at her lemonade stand.
   Monday   25¢
   Tuesday   46¢
   Wednesday 54¢
   Thursday   85¢
   Friday   55¢
   What were her average daily earnings for the five days? _____

8. In one family, people are the following ages: 11, 15, 34, 39, and 81.

   What is the average age? _____

9. There are five boys on a basketball team. Their heights are given below.
   Slammin' Sam   2 feet tall
   Elmo   8 feet tall
   The Rocket   4 feet tall
   The Hook   6 feet tall
   Hammer   10 feet tall
   What is the average height of the team? _____

Finding the Average 4

Solve the following problems.

1. What is the average of 3, 5, 7, 9, and 16? _____

2. What is the average of 600 and 900? _____

3. What is the average of 547, 928, and 1,003? _____

4. A taxi driver makes the following amounts during a week of driving.

   Monday $24.50
   Tuesday $21.35
   Wednesday $34.75
   Thursday $15.00
   Friday $45.46
   Saturday $20.40

   What is his average daily income for the six days? _____

5. In seven different games, a basketball player makes the following scores.

   First game   43 points
   Second game   23 points
   Third game   60 points
   Fourth game   26 points
   Fifth game   87 points
   Sixth game   33 points
   Seventh game 22 points

   What is her average score for the seven games? _____

6. Manuel earned $11,254 one summer and $14,368 the next.

   What is the average he made for the 2 summers? _____

40

Test 6—Finding the Average

Work out the problems on this page.

1. Find the average of 14, 17, 19, 29, and 36. _____

2. Find the average of 300 and 800. _____

3. A man works selling books from door to door. In one week, he sells the following amounts.

   Monday   14
   Tuesday   12
   Wednesday   9
   Thursday   35
   Friday   2
   Saturday   24

   What is his average daily sale of books that week? _____

4. LaShonda works for five months and makes the following amounts.

   February $326
   March $521
   April $112
   May $400
   June $231

   What is her average monthly earning for those months? _____

5. On his spelling tests a boy made the following scores.

   Test 1   96%
   Test 2   60%
   Test 3   75%
   Test 4   79%
   Test 5   95%

   What was his average score? _____

1. Find the interval, and then figure out what *A* is on each of the following number lines.

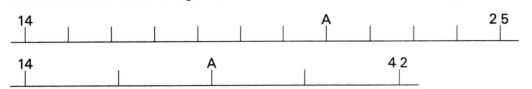

A =_____

A =_____

2. Write 907 using words. _____

   Write seven hundred eighty using numbers. _____

3. Circle the numbers that are prime.

   2, 3, 4, 5, 6, 7, 8, 9, 10, 11, 12, 13, 14, 15, 16, 17, 18, 19, 20, 21

4. Apply the four steps used in division to solve the following two problems.

   6202 ÷ 7 = _____

   3624 ÷ 6 = _____

Unit 7—Place Value 1

Look at the big number below and learn the *place values.*

$$\underset{\text{trillions}}{\overbrace{21}},\underset{\text{billions}}{\overbrace{462}},\underset{\text{millions}}{\overbrace{315}},\underset{\text{thousands}}{\overbrace{301}},\underset{\substack{\text{hundreds}\\\text{tens}\\\text{ones}}}{9\ 8\ 6}$$

Answer the following questions about the big number above. Answer in words.

1. How many thousands are there? _____ thousands

2. How many trillions are there? _____ trillions

3. How many hundreds are there? _____ hundreds

4. How many millions are there? _____ millions

5. How many tens are there? _____ tens

6. How many billions are there? _____ billions

7. How many ones are there? _____ ones

Use words to answer the following questions.

8. How many thousands are there in 54,821? _____ thousands

9. How many tens are there in 43,850? _____ tens

10. How many millions are there in 23,410,354? _____ millions

11. How many ones are there in 342,579? _____ ones

12. How many billions are there in 25,345,101,292? _____ billions

13. How many thousands are there in 243,546,910,243,321? _____

_____ thousands

Now write the following numbers as words.

Example:

    41,000 ___forty-one thousand_____

14. 29,000,000 _____

15. 15,000,000,000 _____

16. 71,000,000,000,000 _____

17. 351,000,000 _____

18. 225,000 _____

Write the following place values on the correct lines above the numbers.
Choose your answers from the list below.

ones
tens
hundreds
thousands
millions
billions
trillions

164, 362, 983, 035, 2 7 3

Use words to answer the following questions about the big number above.

Example: How many thousands are in the big number? _____ thirty-five thousand _____

1. How many billions? _____

2. How many tens? _____

3. How many hundreds? _____

4. How many millions? _____

5. How many trillions? _____

6. How many ones? _____

Use words to answer the following questions.

7. How many thousands in 32,457,648,211? _____

8. How many tens in 32,470? _____

9. How many millions in 54,981,001,213? _____

10. How many hundreds in 34,576,960? _____

Now write the following numbers as words.

11. 35,000,000 _____

12. 421,000 _____

13. 900,000,000,000 _____

14. 314,000,000,000,000 _____

Now write the following words as numbers.

15. two hundred fifteen thousand _____

16. nineteen million _____

1. Find the average of 13, 28, and 7.

   _____

2. Find the average of 35, 12, 13, 10, and 45.

   _____

3. Find the average of 300 and 450.

   _____

4. Write down the two steps you use to find an average.

   1) _____

   2) _____

   _____

5. $(8 \times 7) + (4 \times 3) + (10 \times 10) =$ _____

6. $(9 \times 4) +$ _____ $= 100$

Find the interval, and then figure out what A should be on each of the following number lines.

7. 17   A   22
    |__|__|__|__|__|__|

    A = _____

8. 27   A   72
    |__|__|__|__|__|__|

    A = _____

9. Factor 100 four ways.

   _____   _____

   _____   _____

10. $49072 \div 8 =$ _____

11. $4944 \div 6 =$ _____

12. $4368 \div 7 =$ _____

13. $4172 \div 5 =$ _____

14. $25215 \div 7 =$ _____

15. $4219 \div 6 =$ _____

Circle the prime numbers.

16. 1   2   3   4   5   6   7   8   9 10
    11 12 13 14 15 16 17 18 19 20
    21 22 23 24 25 26 27 28 29 30
    31 32 33 34 35 36 37 38 39 40

17. A train is chugging along at a steady speed of 48 miles an hour. How far can it go in 9 hours?

    _____

18. An elevator has a capacity of 1,000 pounds. Several people get on it. They are Michael, who weighs 247 pounds; Jose, who weighs 145 pounds; Brenda, who weighs 121 pounds; Big Eddie, who weighs 399 pounds; and Slim Jim, who weighs 81 pounds. Is the elevator overloaded? Explain.

    _____

    _____

19. A man wins $1,512. He decides to divide the money evenly among his 7 children. How much does each of the children get?

    _____

Write in the place values on the
lines above the numbers
to the right.

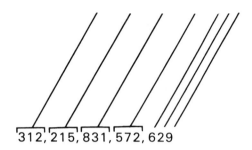

312,215,831,572,629

Use words to answer the following questions about the number above.

1. How many hundreds are there? _____

2. How many billions are there? _____

3. How many thousands? _____

4. How many millions? _____

5. How many ones? _____

6. How many trillions? _____

7. How many tens? _____

Now write the following numbers as words.

8. 44,000,000 _____

9. 350,000 _____

10. 218,000,000,000 _____

11. 875,000,000,000,000 _____

12. 367,000,000 _____

Now write the following words as numbers.

13. twenty-four million _____

14. five hundred thirty-eight thousand _____

15. seven hundred fifty-three million _____

16. two hundred thousand _____

17. six hundred eighteen trillion _____

**Put commas in the following number. Start at the *right* and work to the *left*. Put a comma after
every three numbers. Then on the line below the number, write how many millions there are.**

18. 2 5 6 8 9 4 3 7 8 4 0 2 9 1 0 5

_____

Place Value 4

Put commas in the number below. Start at the right and work to the left. Put a comma after every three numbers.

6 3 9 4 7 8 9 3 5 6 0 1 2 3 5 7

Use words to answer the following questions about the number above.

1. How many thousands? _____

2. How many millions? _____

3. How many ones? _____

4. How many trillions? _____

_____

5. How many tens? _____

6. How many billions? _____

7. How many hundreds? _____

Write the following numbers as words.

8. 39,000,000 _____

9. 215,000 _____

10. 437,000,000,000,000 _____

11. 298,000,000,000 _____

12. 501,000 _____

Write the following words as numbers.

13. eight hundred seventy-three million _____

14. three hundred eighteen trillion _____

15. one hundred eleven thousand _____

16. twenty-five billion _____

17. two hundred seventeen thousand _____

Put commas in the number below.

3 5 8 2 1 3 1 4 6 2 9 2 9 7

Use words to answer the following questions about the number above.

1. How many tens in the number? _____

2. How many millions? _____

3. How many trillions? _____

4. How many ones? _____

5. How many hundreds? _____

6. How many thousands? _____

7. How many billions? _____

Write the following numbers as words.

8. 35,000 _____

9. 245,000,000,000,000 _____

10. 701,000,000 _____

11. 815,000,000,000 _____

Write the following words as numbers.

12. six hundred fifty-three million _____

13. two hundred forty-eight thousand _____

14. nine hundred billion _____

15. six hundred twelve trillion _____

16. nineteen thousand _____

17. twelve million _____

18. eight hundred ninety-seven billion _____

19. seventy-five million _____

Circle the number that has two hundred nineteen millions.

20. 219,000,678,245   684,291,371,428

    209,000,381   846,349,219,384,021

1. Find the interval, and then figure out what *A* is on each of the following number lines.

   A = _____

   A = _____

2. Write 917 using words. _____

   Write two hundred nineteen using numbers. _____

3. Factor 12 two ways. _____   _____

   Factor 30 two ways. _____   _____

4. 3437 ÷ 6 = _____

   3990 ÷ 7 = _____

5. Find the average of 74, 48, and 19. _____

   Find the average of 103 and 205. _____

The numbers to the right of the decimal point (.) are called *decimals.* Learn the place values used with decimals.

Place Values

. 0 0 0 0 0

decimal point
tenths
hundredths
thousandths
ten-thousandths
hundred-thousandths

Use words to give the place values of each of the following decimals.

.3 _____ three tenths _____

1. .03 _____

2. .003 _____

3. .5 _____

4. .007 _____

5. .12 _____

6. .0012 _____

_____

7. .1 _____

8. .00004 _____

_____

9. .55 _____

Write the following words as decimals. Use numbers and decimal points.

six tenths _____ .6 _____

10. six hundredths _____

11. six thousandths _____

12. two hundredths _____

13. seven hundred-thousandths_____

14. eight tenths _____

15. nine hundredths _____

16. five ten-thousandths _____

17. seventeen hundredths _____

18. twelve thousandths _____

First, use words to write the following fractions. Then write each as a decimal.

$\frac{2}{10}$ _____ two tenths _____ .2

19. $\frac{3}{10,000}$ _____ _____

_____

20. $\frac{4}{1,000}$ _____ _____

_____

21. $\frac{13}{100}$ _____ _____

_____

22. $\frac{9}{1,000}$ _____ _____

_____

23. $\frac{7}{100}$ _____ _____

_____

Place Values

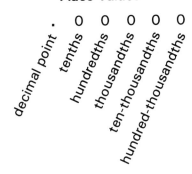

Use words to write the following decimals.

.02 _____ two hundredths _____

1. .005 _____

2. .9 _____

3. .0009 _____
_____

4. .07 _____

5. .001 _____

6. .3 _____

7. .11 _____

8. .00011 _____
_____

9. .082 _____
_____

Now write the following words as decimals. Use numbers and decimal points.

two tenths _____ .2 _____

10. two hundredths _____

11. two thousandths _____

12. six hundredths _____

13. twelve hundredths _____

14. twelve ten-thousandths _____

15. six tenths _____

16. sixteen thousandths _____

17. forty-five hundredths _____

18. sixty-two thousandths _____

Write the following fractions as decimals. Use numbers and decimal points.

19. $\dfrac{4}{100}$ _____

20. $\dfrac{6}{10}$ _____

21. $\dfrac{2}{1,000}$ _____

22. $\dfrac{17}{100,000}$ _____

23. $\dfrac{9}{10}$ _____

First use words to write the following decimals. Then write the fraction without using a decimal point.

Example:

.02 _____ two hundredths _____ $\dfrac{2}{100}$

24. .8 _____ _____

25. .09 _____ _____

26. .007 _____ _____
_____

27. .11 _____
_____

28. .011 _____ _____
_____

29. .931 _____
_____

30. .017 _____ _____
_____

Review 8

Write the following numbers as words.

1. 54,000,000 _____

   _____

2. 29,000,000,000,000 _____

   _____

3. 301,000 _____

   _____

4. 254,000,000,000 _____

   _____

Write the following words as numbers.

5. seventeen trillion

   _____

6. twenty-nine thousand

   _____

7. four hundred seventeen million

   _____

8. ninety-two billion

   _____

Put commas in the correct places in the number below. On the line write how many millions are in the number.

9. 34612002499824183

   _____

   _____

10. $(8 \times 5) + (9 \times 4) + (10 \times 3) =$ _____

11. $(7 \times 6) +$ _____ $= 100$

Find the interval and then figure out what A should be on the line below.

12.
```
20                 A           45
 |   |   |   |   |   |   |
```

   A = _____

Factor 36 four ways.

13. _____   _____

    _____   _____

14. $24512 \div 8 =$ _____

15. $42583 \div 7 =$ _____

16. Find the average of 21, 60, and 27.

    _____

17. Find the average of 15, 47, 29, and 33.

    _____

18. Find the average of 197 and 211.

    _____

19. There are 3 people on a team. Sandra weighs 366 pounds; Stu weighs 244 pounds; and Jo-Jo weighs 203 pounds. What is the average weight of the people on the team?

    _____

20. A woman makes $47 a day. How much does she make in 8 days of work?

    _____

21. A man makes $19,365 in 1 year. He has to pay $7,356 in taxes to the federal government. How much does he have left after taxes?

    _____

Decimal Place Value 3

Use words to write the following numbers. Write the whole number first; then write *and* when you get to the decimal point.

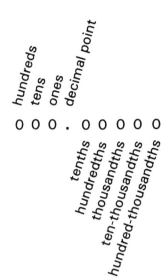

2.4 _____ two and four tenths _____

1. 3.04 _____

2. 1.001 _____

   _____

3. 4.09 _____

   _____

4. 2.003 _____

   _____

5. 8.2 _____

   _____

   _____

6. 12.02 _____

   _____

7. 16.0006 _____

   _____

8. 11.02 _____

   _____

9. 6.016 _____

   _____

10. 25.25 _____

    _____

11. 4.014 _____

    _____

Write the following words as decimals.

12. two and three tenths _____

13. six and one hundredth _____

14. twelve and one tenth _____

15. seven and six hundred-thousandths

    _____

16. two and two hundredths _____

17. sixteen and six thousandths _____

18. two and four tenths _____

19. forty-five and sixteen thousandths

    _____

Change the following to decimals.

$2\frac{7}{10}$ _____ 2.7 _____

20. $3\frac{7}{10,000}$ _____

21. $4\frac{3}{100}$ _____

22. $7\frac{14}{1,000}$ _____

Now change these to fractions.

.07 = $\frac{7}{100}$ 25. .013 = _____

23. .45 = _____   26. .971 = _____

24. .001 = _____   27. .4 = _____

Use words to write the following numbers. Write the whole number first; then write *and* when you get to the decimal point.

1. 4.05 _____

2. 3.001 _____

3. 7.21 _____

4. 9.004 _____

5. 28.01 _____

6. 9.11 _____

7. 80.005 _____

8. 12.013 _____

9. 2.016 _____

10. 26.001 _____

Write the following decimals as fractions.

11. .01 _____   12. .9 _____   13. .003 _____   14. .137 _____

Write the following words as decimals.

15. seventeen and six tenths _____

16. twelve and two hundredths _____

17. six and four thousandths _____

18. nine and sixty-three hundredths _____

19. twenty-seven and forty-seven thousandths _____

20. fifty-four and seven tenths _____

21. two hundred and six hundredths _____

22. forty-two and sixteen thousandths _____

Change the following to decimals.

23. $6\frac{2}{10}$ _____ 24. $4\frac{23}{100}$ _____ 25. $7\frac{2}{1000}$ _____ 26. $8\frac{13}{100}$ _____

27. $12\frac{1}{100}$ _____ 28. $40\frac{2}{1000}$ _____ 29. $310\frac{5}{100}$ _____ 30. $51\frac{6}{10}$ _____

Write the following numbers as words.

1. 3.1 _____

2. 4.02 _____

3. 1.005 _____

4. 12.09 _____

5. 24.11 _____

6. 2.032 _____

7. 40.2 _____

8. 3.017 _____

Write the following words as numbers.

9. six and two hundredths _____

10. two and four tenths _____

11. twelve and sixteen hundredths _____

12. sixty-four and two hundredths _____

13. nine and fourteen thousandths _____

14. twenty-four and six thousandths _____

15. ninety-nine and ninety-nine hundredths _____

Write the following as decimals.

16. $2 \frac{4}{100}$ _____

17. $6 \frac{23}{1000}$ _____

18. $28 \frac{9}{10}$ _____

19. $3 \frac{9}{100}$ _____

20. $19 \frac{19}{1000}$ _____

1. Find the interval, and then figure out what *A* is on the following number line.

15   A   30   A = _____

2. Write 794,000 in words. _____

_____

Write six hundred ninety million in numbers. _____

3. Factor 28 two ways. _____ _____

4. 2546 ÷ 7 = _____

5. Find the average of 63, 81, 72, 40, and 24. _____

Unit 9 — Adding and Subtracting Decimals 1

To add or subtract decimals, stack up the numbers with the decimal points in line. Then add or subtract.

Example: 3.456 − 1.21

Step one:
```
  3.456
− 1.21
```
.   Decimal point moves down

Step two:
```
  3.456
− 1.21
  2.246  Answer
```

Now do the following problems. Follow the steps shown above.
Remember: You may need to borrow in subtraction problems.

1. 25.61 − 3.21

2. 296.42 + 5.1

3. 385.2 + 49.6

4. 24.64 − 5.23

5. 854.2 + 35.1

6. 656.42 − 5.39

7. 296.3 − 54.4

8. 289.6 + 38.4

9. 496.27 + 38.37

10. 294.65 − 59.1

11. 5842.6 − 35.9

Now do this problem by following the same steps.

12. At the beginning of a trip to Atlanta, your
car's odometer read 18,354.3 miles.
When you got to Atlanta, it read
19,063.1.
How far did you drive?

_____ miles

Adding and Subtracting Decimals 2

Remember: To add or subtract decimals, line up the decimal points first.

Example: 24.95 − 3.9

```
  24.95
−  3.9
  21.05  Answer
```

Do the following problems.

1. 2.5 − 1.3

2. 2.56 + 1.3

3. 8.39 + 1.41

4. 21.39 − 1.56

5. 85.62 − 1.39

6. 11.39 − 2.4

7. 8.24 + 1.3

8. 4.963 − 2.9

You can add zeroes (0s) after the last number following a decimal point without changing the value of the number.

Example: 6.2 = 6.20
6.2 = 6.200
but   6.2 is not 6.02!

Circle *T* (true) or *F* (false).

9. 5.61 = 5.610   T   F

10. 5.61 = 5.061   T   F

11. 5.61 = 5.601   T   F

12. 4.2 = 4.200   T   F

13. 5.73 = 5.073   T   F

14. 5.703 = 5.7030   T   F

15. 6.21 = 6.21000   T   F

16. 6.30 = 6.3   T   F

17. 6.301 = 6.3010   T   F

18. 8.402 = 8.420   T   F

Add two 0s (zeroes) to each of these so that the value of the number stays the same.

19. 5.3 _____

20. 6.41 _____

21. 8.935 _____

22. 10.301 _____

23. 4.02 _____

24. 5.039 _____

25. 6.0301 _____

26. 8.643 _____

27. 9.02 _____

Review 9

Write the following numbers as words.

1. 9.1 _____

_____

2. 1.004 _____

_____

3. 19.012 _____

_____

4. 1.23 _____

_____

Write the following words as decimals.

5. two and three thousandths

_____

6. four and eleven hundredths

_____

7. one and one tenth

_____

8. five and thirteen thousandths

_____

Find the interval, and then figure out what _A_ is on the following line.

9.
```
12        A              22
|||||||||||||||
```

A = _____

10. Factor 80 four ways.

_____ _____

_____ _____

11. 50560 ÷ 8 = _____

12. 42589 ÷ 7 = _____

13. Find the average of 99 and 87.

_____

14. Find the average of 38, 46, 22, and 30.

_____

Write the following numbers as words.

15. 215,000,000 _____

_____

16. 630,000 _____

_____

17. 714,000,000,000,000 _____

_____

18. 48,000,000,000 _____

_____

Write the following words as numbers.

19. twelve billion

_____

20. four hundred seventeen trillion

_____

21. two hundred three million

_____

22. A cab driver made $37 on Monday, $48 on Tuesday, $60 on Wednesday, $34 on Thursday, $3 on Friday, and $94 on Saturday. How much did he make all together?

_____

23. What was the cab driver's average daily earning?

_____

24. A girl eats 7 bags of onion-flavored potato chips a day. How many bags does she eat a year? (There are 365 days in a year.)

_____

Sometimes you need to add zeroes (0s) before you can subtract.

Example:

$$6.3 - 4.21 = \begin{array}{r} 6.3 \\ -4.21 \\ \hline \end{array} = \begin{array}{r} 6.30 \\ -4.21 \\ \hline 2.09 \end{array} \quad \text{Answer}$$

Do the following problems. Remember to add zeroes (0s) when you need to.

1. $2.5 - 1.48$

2. $3.6 - 1.25$

3. $10.3 - 4.21$

4. $15.6 - 5.29$

5. $24.54 - 3.1$

6. $64.28 + 3.1$

7. $64.1 - 3.28$

8. $56.75 + 3.11$

9. $4.02 - 3.001$

10. $5.63 - 2.002$

11. $5.1 - 4.209$

12. $6.2 - 3.44$

Now do the following word problem.

13. You had $5.65. You spent $1.95 on gum. How much money do you have left?

_____

A number always has a decimal point, but sometimes you can't see it. If you can't, it's at the end of the number.

Example:

4 is 4.
and
6239 is 6239.

Supply the decimal points in the numbers below.

4   21   310   4286

Study the following subtraction examples.

Example:

4 − 1.3   4.   You supply the decimal point.   4.0   Add a zero.
           −1.3   −1.3

Example: Example:

5 − 3.44   5.00   6.4 − 3   6.4
            −3.44   −3.
            ─────   ─────
             1.56   Answer   3.4   Answer

Do the following problems.

1. 6 − 3.4   2. 12 − 5.2   3. 35 − 3.1   4. 240 − 5.1

5. 295 − 290.4   6. 56.2 − 3.48   7. 5.48 + 3.2   8. 10.2 − 6

9. 51 − 39.7   10. 40 + 30.5   11. 21.46 − 3.111   12. 25 − 3.11

13. 46 − 2.14   14. 30 − 1.01   15. 25.671 + 4

Test 9—Adding and Subtracting Decimals

Do all the following problems.

1.   4.29
      + 1.13

2.   15.35
      −   4.2

3.   403.6
      +   2.71

4.   29
      −   .49

Now do these problems.

5. 56.56 + 3.42

6. 249.45 − 5.9

7. 606.06 + .6

8. 29.9 + 3.111

9. 50 − 3.2

10. 243 − .6

1. Find the interval, and then figure out what _A_ is on the following number line.

8   A   28

A = _____

2. Write 78,000,000 in words. _____

Write 214,000,000,000,000 in words. _____

_____

Write sixty-five thousand in numbers. _____

Write nine hundred six billion in numbers. _____

3. Factor 40 three ways. _____   _____   _____

4. 48295 ÷ 8 = _____

5. Find the average of 8, 23, 15, and 26. _____

6. Use words to write 2.003. _____

Use numbers to write one and thirteen hundredths. _____

Use the number line below to *round off* the following numbers to the nearest ten. You must decide which ten is closer to the number — the one up or the one down.

Example:

77 rounded off to the nearest ten is 80 because 77 is closer to 80 than it is to 70.

```
    60                              70                              80
 59  |  61 62 63 64 65 66 67 68 69  |  71 72 73 74 75 76 77 78 79  |  81 82 83 84 85 86 87
 |   |   |  |  |  |  |  |  |  |  |   |   |  |  |  |  |  |  |  |  |   |   |  |  |  |  |  |  |
```

1. 64 _____ (Is it closer to 60 or 70?)

2. 76 _____ (Is it closer to 70 or 80?)

3. 71 _____

4. 83 _____

5. 66 _____

6. 59 _____

7. 75 _____ (5 goes up to the higher ten.)

8. 69 _____

9. 84 _____

10. 65 _____

11. 61 _____

12. 79 _____

13. 82 _____

14. 62 _____

Without using a number line, round off the following numbers to the nearest ten.
Remember:

```
   ←——— down        ———— up ——→
   1   2   3   4     5   6   7   8   9
```

15. 46 _____ (Between __40__ and __50__;
            closer to which?)

16. 33 _____ (Between _____ and _____;
            closer to which?)

17. 94 _____

18. 22 _____

19. 16 _____

20. 54 _____

21. 55 _____

22. 99 _____

23. 88 _____

24. 51 _____

25. 45 _____

26. 87 _____

27. 22 _____

Now round off the following numbers to the nearest 100. (Look at the tens place to decide what each answer should be.)

28. 142 _____ (Between __100__ and __200__;
             closer to which?)

29. 489 _____ (Between _____ and _____;
             closer to which?)

30. 827 _____

31. 421 _____

Rounding Off Numbers 2

Remember two things as you round off numbers:

1)
```
      down              up
   1  2  3  4     5  6  7  8  9
```

2) When you are trying to decide whether to go up or down, always look one place value to the right to decide which way to go.
For example, if you are rounding off a number to the nearest thousand, look at the hundreds place.

thousands hundreds tens ones
55, 3 0 1

Round off the numbers below to the nearest ten.

1. 18 _____
    between _____ and _____

2. 24 _____

3. 93 _____

4. 35 _____

5. 29 _____

6. 21 _____

7. 86 _____

8. 75 _____

9. 38 _____

10. 54 _____

11. 12 _____

12. 98 _____

13. 73 _____

14. 81 _____

Round off the numbers below to the nearest hundred.

15. 732 _____
    between _____ and _____

16. 367 _____

17. 899 _____

18. 281 _____

19. 549 _____

20. 118 _____

21. 929 _____

22. 551 _____

23. 781 _____

24. 438 _____

25. 191 _____

26. 425 _____

27. 333 _____

28. 952 _____

29. 381 _____

Round off the numbers below to the nearest thousand.

30. 3,231 _____
    between _____ and _____

31. 5,387 _____

32. 1,735 _____

33. 2,111 _____

34. 4,298 _____

35. 5,432 _____

36. 6,592 _____

37. 5,102 _____

38. 4,298 _____

39. 4,104 _____

40. 2,555 _____

41. 6,500 _____

42. 2,323 _____

43. 11,531 _____

44. 34,231 _____

Do the following problems.

45. Andy makes $1,929 a month. In 3 months how much does he make? Round off your answer to the nearest thousand.

_____

46. A dairy produces 174 eggs a day. In 7 days, how many eggs does it produce? Round off your answer to the nearest hundred.

_____

1. $63.9 + 4.38 + 293 =$ _____

2. $44.5 + 87 + 2.001 =$ _____

3. $556 + 2.3 + .882 =$ _____

4. $67.4 - 21.431 =$ _____

5. $12.8 - 1.437 =$ _____

6. $735 - 1.529 =$ _____

Find the interval, and then figure out what A is on the following line.

7.
```
    20                    A     28
    |___|____|____|____|____|
```

A = _____

Write the following numbers in words.

8. 83,000,000,000 _____

_____

9. 207,000 _____

_____

Write the following words as numbers.

10. nine hundred one trillion

_____

11. four hundred million

_____

12. Factor 24 three ways.

_____

_____

13. $30582 \div 6 =$ _____

14. Find the average of 271 and 903.

_____

Write the following numbers in words.

15. 2.03 _____

_____

16. 7.1 _____

_____

17. 4.005 _____

_____

18. 2.11 _____

_____

Write the following words in numbers.

19. five and twelve thousandths

_____

20. one and one hundredth

_____

21. Larry sells newspapers. On Monday he made $23.45; on Tuesday he made $35.00; on Wednesday he made $13.25. What were his total earnings for the 3 days?

_____

22. An old beat-up propeller plane goes 592 miles in 4 hours. How far does it go each hour?

_____

23. A bank had $379,218,100 in its vault. Then it was robbed of $25,693,245. How much was left in the vault?

_____

24. The principal of a school decided to give $5 to each of the 618 students in the school. How much money did she decide to give away?

_____

Rounding Off Numbers 3

Round off the numbers below to the nearest ten.

16 __20__

1. 54 _____

2. 39 _____

3. 53 _____

4. 43 _____

5. 96 _____

6. 39 _____

7. 28 _____

8. 41 _____

9. 32 _____

10. 55 _____

Round off the numbers below to the nearest hundred.

746 __700__

11. 329 _____

12. 386 _____

13. 466 _____

14. 371 _____

15. 388 _____

16. 334 _____

17. 722 _____

18. 299 _____

19. 281 _____

20. 332 _____

Round off the numbers below to the nearest million.

3,423,985 __3,000,000__

21. 4,119,942 _____

22. 7,455,232 _____

23. 6,768,099 _____

24. 2,313,222 _____

25. 7,432,676 _____

26. 2,500,343 _____

27. 4,878,101 _____

28. 3,245,868 _____

29. 1,127,578 _____

30. 24,249,022 _____

Remember to look one place value to the right of the decimal.

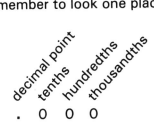

.   0   0   0

Round off these decimals to the nearest tenth.

.26439 _____.3_____

31. .43543 _____

32. .78221 _____

33. .55631 _____

34. .67222 _____

35. .32289 _____

36. .67556 _____

Round off these decimals to the nearest hundredth.

.435234 _____.44_____

37. .254371 _____

38. .878633 _____

39. .576939 _____

40. .212326 _____

41. .434652 _____

42. .356453 _____

Rounding Off Numbers 4

Round off the numbers to the nearest ten.

1. 24 _____

2. 58 _____

3. 83 _____

4. 75 _____

5. 27 _____

6. 97 _____

7. 72 _____

Round off the numbers to the nearest hundred.

8. 746 _____

9. 687 _____

10. 399 _____

11. 251 _____

12. 931 _____

13. 365 _____

14. 374 _____

Round off the numbers to the nearest thousand.

15. 8,324 _____

16. 6,549 _____

17. 2,314 _____

18. 6,502 _____

19. 5,999 _____

20. 3,671 _____

21. 4,218 _____

Round off the numbers to the nearest tenth.

22. .24316 _____

23. .67453 _____

24. .54627 _____

25. .24315 _____

26. .79576 _____

27. .24325 _____

28. .87956 _____

Round off the numbers to the nearest million.

29. 4,354,678 _____

30. 3,654,890 _____

31. 2,246,111 _____

32. 8,795,253 _____

33. 14,365,666 _____

34. 57,564,769 _____

Round off the numbers to the nearest billion.

35. 8,342,576,887 _____

36. 1,546,887,593 _____

37. 3,555,476,998 _____

38. 7,324,154,734 _____

39. 9,763,656,259 _____

40. 1,223,530,239 _____

Solve the following problems.

41. A farm grows 3,657 bushels of wheat. Rounded off to the nearest thousand, how many bushels is that?

_____

42. At one point the population of the United States was 209,654,768. Rounded off to the nearest million, what was the population?

_____

Round off the numbers to the nearest ten.

1. 15 _____

2. 74 _____

3. 36 _____

4. 38 _____

5. 72 _____

6. 24 _____

Round off the numbers to the nearest hundred.

7. 845 _____

8. 469 _____

9. 261 _____

10. 971 _____

11. 785 _____

12. 358 _____

Round off the numbers to the nearest thousand.

13. 5,498 _____

14. 4,879 _____

15. 1,242 _____

16. 8,644 _____

17. 2,501 _____

18. 19,354 _____

Round off the numbers to the nearest tenth.

19. .25447 _____

20. .43557 _____

21. .87967 _____

22. .53427 _____

23. .77684 _____

24. .56332 _____

Round off the numbers to the nearest million.

25. 4,653,889 _____

26. 2,368,564 _____

27. 9,561,001 _____

28. 67,326,871 _____

Round off the numbers to the nearest billion.

29. 8,643,667,217 _____

30. 8,974,112,310 _____

31. 7,436,547,291 _____

32. 6,500,000,001 _____

Solve the following problem.

33. The population of a country is 23,754,769 people. Rounded off to the nearest million, what is the population?

_____

1. Find the interval, and then figure out what *A* is on the following number line.

16   A   2 8

A = _____

2. Use words to write 68,000,000,000. _____

Use numbers to write seven hundred four million. _____

3. Factor 56 three ways. _____ _____ _____

4. 72308 ÷ 9 = _____

5. Find the average of 296 and 306. _____

6. Use words to write 3.05. _____

Use numbers to write seven and eleven thousandths. _____

7. 35 + 283.19 = _____

8. 5.9 − 3.186 = _____

To multiply, follow the steps below.

1) Multiply by the first number. (In the example below, it is 3.)

2) Multiply by the second number. (In the example below, it is 2.) Move the answer over one place to the left.

3) Draw a line and add to get the answer.

Example:

```
  421          421          421          421
×  23        ×  23        ×  23        ×  23
             1263         1263         1263
                           842        + 842
                                       9,683  Answer
```

Use the multiplication steps shown above to do the following problems.

1.
```
  821
×  35
```

2.
```
  345
×  82
```

3.
```
  209
×  64
```

4.
```
  219
×  83
```

5.
```
  362
×  67
```

6.
```
  814
×  29
```

7.
```
  204
×  82
```

8.
```
  1345
×   63
```

Now solve the following two problems.

9. A man's heart beats 63 times a minute. How many times does it beat in 25 minutes?

_____

10. Rosa makes $428 a week. How much can she make in 12 weeks?

_____

Two-Number and Three-Number Multiplication 2

Use the multiplication steps you have learned to solve the following problems. See if you can get them all right!

1.	263 × 38	2.	412 × 89	

3.	428 × 67	4.	203 × 136

5.	435 × 91	6.	499 × 218	7.	1776 × 36	8.	2236 × 87

Solve the following problems.

9. A train is going 58 miles an hour. If it keeps going at that speed for 24 hours, how far will it have traveled?

_____

10. A jet travels at 563 miles an hour. How far can it travel in 15 hours?

11. Tamara works after school and makes $437 a month. How much can she make in a year (12 months)?

_____

12. A factory makes 3,490 cars a day. How many cars can it make in 23 days?

_____

Review 11

Round off the following numbers to the nearest thousand.

1. 4,793 _____

2. 17,924 _____

3. 2,362 _____

4. 67,245 _____

Round off the following decimals to the nearest hundredth.

5. .475981 _____

6. .9333333 _____

7. .749511 _____

8. .428932 _____

Round off the following decimals to the nearest thousandth.

9. .934789 _____

10. .666666 _____

11. .333333 _____

12. .472143 _____

Round off the following decimals to the nearest one.

13. 7.943721 _____

14. 2.389472 _____

15. Write 920,000,000,000 in words.

_____

_____

16. Write sixteen million in numbers.

_____

17. Factor 24. _____

18. 48205 ÷ 6 = _____

19. Find the average of 99 and 115.

_____

Write the following numbers in words.

20. 4.07 _____

21. 1.011 _____

Write the following words in numbers.

22. five and one thousandth _____

23. seven and five tenths _____

24. 42.8 + 3.975 = _____

25. 5.93 + 85.003 = _____

26. 35 + 8.73 = _____

27. 9.3 − 4.154 = _____

28. 13.7 − 1.148 = _____

29. Jammin' Julie, the great basketball star, scored 35 points in one game, 83 points in another, 44 points in another, and 62 points in another. What was her average per game?

_____

30. Cynthia got $18.35 from her mother and $13.50 from her grandmother, but then she lost $14.00 on the bus. How much did she have left?

_____

31. Alex made $1,233 in 9 weeks. How much did he make each week?

_____

32. A jet goes 605 miles an hour. How far can it go in 7 hours?

_____

73

Two-Number and Three-Number Multiplication 3

Carefully work out the following problems. Use the multiplication steps you have learned.

1.
```
    216
  ×  83
```

2.
```
    625
  ×  74
```

3.
```
    209
  ×  95
```

4.
```
    386
  × 381
```

5.
```
    289
  ×  73
```

6.
```
    330
  × 446
```

7.
```
    895
  ×  77
```

8.
```
    362
  ×  90
```

Solve the following problems.

9. A student makes $135 a week. How much money can she make if she works for 48 weeks of the year?

_____

10. At top speed, a race car's engine turns around 6,500 times each minute. How many times does it turn around going top speed for 24 minutes?

_____

11. Vanessa has $3,500. She says she wants to have 15 times that much. How much money does she want to have?

_____

12. In the middle of a race, David's heart is beating 136 times a minute. How many times will it beat if he keeps running for 14 minutes?

_____

Using the multiplication steps you have learned, carefully work out the following problems.

1.	289 × 73	2.	365 × 48	3.	238 × 590	4.	827 × 63

5.	1267 × 76	6.	2408 × 338	7.	1642 × 36	8.	6937 × 86

Now solve the following problems.

9. Mario saves $528 a month. How much does he save in a year (12 months)?

_____

10. A family buys a used car on the installment plan. They have to make 36 payments of $125 each. How much will the car cost in all?

_____

11. A car is going 73 miles an hour. At this speed, how far will it go in 24 hours?

_____

12. A woman had 12 children. When she died she gave each child $450. Altogether how much did she give her children?

_____

Carefully work out all of the following problems.

1.	342	2.	491	3.	607	4.	948
	× 35		× 84		× 26		× 479

5.	647	6.	1403	7.	7947	8.	4964
	× 29		× 21		× 206		× 517

Solve the following problems.

9. Allison buys a computer and has to pay for it in 24 payments. Each payment is $155. How much will the computer cost her by the time she has made all the payments?

_____

10. Valerie makes $156 a day. How much will she make in 7 weeks (49 days)?

_____

1. Find the interval, and then figure out what *A* is on the following number line.

18   A   48   A = _____

2. Write 604,000,000 in words. _____

    Write twenty-five trillion in numbers. _____

3. Factor 30 three ways. _____   _____   _____

4. 66435 ÷ 8 = _____

5. Find the average of 35, 68, and 41. _____

6. Write 9.5 in words. _____

    Write seven and four thousandths in decimals. _____

7. 68.5 + 4.391 = _____

8. 23.4 − 9.153 = _____

9. Round off 7,694,284 to the nearest million. _____

10. Round off .5428941 to the nearest hundredth. _____

To multiply decimals, follow the steps listed below.

1) Multiply normally.
2) Count how many numbers there are to the right of the decimal or decimals in the problem.
3) Count off that number of decimal places in the in the answer. Start from the right and move to the left.

Example:

   13.**41**   There are a total of three numbers to the right of the decimals
   × **.2**   in the problem.
   2.**682**   Answer has three decimal places.

Put the decimal in the correct place in each of the following answers.

Example:

   4.**69**   There are a total of three numbers to the right of the decimals
   × **.5**   in the problem, so there are three decimal places
   2.**345**   in the answer.

1.	21.4	2.	365	3.	.369	4.	.284
	× .6		× .9		× 6		× .8
	1284		3285		2214		2272

Work out the following problems. Use the steps listed at the top of this page. Be sure to put the decimal in the correct place in each answer.

5.	74.2	6.	.223	7.	4.29	8.	2.05	9.	.316
	× .6		× .6		× 8		× .4		× 6

10.	362	11.	9.38	12.	.643	13.	83.1	14.	207
	× .4		× 2		× .6		× .9		× .4

Do the next two problems.

15. Luis makes $11.60 an hour. How much can he make if he works 3 hours?

_____

16. A man sends out 7 letters. Each one weighs 1.43 ounces. How much do the letters weigh all together?

_____

Multiplication of Decimals 2

Remember the steps to follow to multiply decimals. If at step three you don't have enough numbers in your answer, add as many zeroes as you need. Add the zeroes to the left of the last number when you count from right to left.

Example:

```
    .415   Four decimal places          .415
  ×  .2    are needed.                 ×  .2
  ───────                              ───────
    830                                .0830   Answer adds a zero to make
                                               four decimal places.
```

Put decimals in the correct places in the following answers. Add zeroes where they are needed.

```
1.    .137      2.   .1286      3.    .214      4.    .135      5.     .146
    ×  .2          ×   .3          ×   .4          ×  .03          ×  .004
    ──────        ───────         ──────          ──────          ──────
     274            3858            856             405             584
```

Now work out the following problems. Add zeroes where they are needed.

```
6.    .273      7.   6.29       8.    .428      9.   6.27      10.   .268
    ×  .5          ×    3           ×   .6          ×  .9          ×  .3
    ──────        ──────          ──────          ─────          ─────
```

```
11.   .174     12.  71.3       13.   .268     14.   489       15.   .613
    ×  .03         ×   .6          ×  .05          ×   .4          ×  .02
    ──────        ──────          ──────          ─────          ──────
```

```
16.  2.43      17.  8.62       18.   .6438
    × .45          × 3.2           ×  .29
    ──────        ──────          ──────
```

Solve the next two problems.

19. Grace makes $3.25 an hour for babysitting.
    How much will she make if she works for
    9 hours?

    _____

20. A box of cereal weighs 12.6 ounces. How
    much do 15 boxes weigh?

    _____

1. $437 \times 93 = $ _____

2. $358 \times 39 = $ _____

3. $47 \times 6019 = $ _____

4. $632 \times 6937 = $ _____

Find the interval, and then figure out what _A_ is on the following number line.

5.

16   A   32

A = _____

6. Write nine hundred forty-seven thousand in numbers.

_____

7. Factors of 63 = _____

8. $56505 \div 8 = $ _____

9. Find the average of 101, 94, 85, 26, and 74.

_____

10. Write 7.004 in words.

_____

_____

11. Write two and fourteen hundredths in numbers.

_____

12. $69 + 2.337 + 903 = $ _____

13. $79.4 - 23.159 = $ _____

Round off the following numbers to the nearest million.

14. 62,479,393 _____

15. 28,547,219 _____

16. 62,188,937 _____

17. 207,235,729 _____

Round off the following to the nearest hundredth.

18. .473593 _____

19. .775934 _____

20. 1.987321 _____

21. 9.74298 _____

22. Marlene's heart beats 75 times a minute while she is sitting down. How many times does it beat in an hour? (An hour has 60 minutes in it.)

_____

23. Mrs. Fischer takes her 3 children to a museum. Her ticket costs $3.50, and each child's ticket costs $1.25. What is the total amount the family pays to get in to the museum?

_____

24. How many pennies can you get for 193 quarters?

_____

25. Mr. Barry's new sports can can go 162 miles on 9 gallons of gasoline. How many miles does his car get to each gallon?

_____

26. A store bought 32 calculators for $34 each. How much did all the calculators cost the store?

_____

Carefully work out the following problems. Be sure to put the decimal in the correct place in each answer. Add zeroes if you need to.

1. 6.04
    × .8

2. 225
    × .7

3. .641
    × 4

4. 293
    × .007

5. .2451
    × .63

6. .235
    × .4

7. .667
    × 5

8. 93.1
    × .8

9. 67.42
    × 8.9

10. 2907
    × .46

11. 69.1
    × .6

12. .297
    × .03

13. .637
    × .04

Solve the following problems.

14. A large apple costs $.46 (46 cents). How much will it cost to buy a year's supply (365 apples)?

    _____

15. A game costs $4.95. How much would 7 of them cost?

    _____

16. A man makes $10.25 an hour as a bricklayer. How much does he make working an 8-hour day?

    _____

Carefully work out the following problems. Be sure to put the decimal in the correct place in each answer. Add zeroes if you need to.

1.	62.1	2.	.283	3.	4.93	4.	3.72	5.	3074
	× .5		× .3		× 8		× .9		× .025

6.	9.73	7.	692	8.	.407	9.	14.38	10.	.4695
	× .4		× .8		× .8		× .69		× .24

11.	.604	12.	.375	13.	.491
	× 8		× .02		× .04

Solve the following problems.

14. A lawyer charges $35.55 an hour. How much will it cost to hire her for 3 hours?

15. A piece of candy costs $.08 (8 cents). How much will it cost to buy 143 candies?

16. A woman bought the same lunch every day, and it cost her $4.35. How much did her lunches cost for a 5-day week?

17. A book weighs 13.7 ounces. How much do 12 copies of the book weigh?

Solve the following problems. Be sure to put the decimal in the correct place in each answer. Add zeroes if you need to.

1. 69.4
    × .5

2. 2.37
    × .4

3. .683
    × 17

4. 23.1
    × .6

5. .146
    × .5

6. 236
    × .9

7. .1472
    × .02

8. 69.47
    × 3.5

Solve the following problems.

9. An iron-worker makes $12.56 an hour. How much does he make working an 8-hour day?

10. A postcard costs $.27 (27 cents). How much would it cost to buy 255 postcards?

1. Find the interval, and then figure out what *A* is on the following number line.

7   A   1 2

A = _____

2. Write 83,000 in words. _____

   Write seven hundred twelve million in numbers. _____

3. Factor 90 three ways. _____   _____   _____

4. $42367 \div 7 =$ _____

5. Find the average of 85, 96, 74, 103, and 62. _____

6. Write 7.06 in words. _____

   Write eight and eleven thousandths in decimals. _____

7. $48 + 29.3 + 2.621 =$ _____

8. $89.4 - 21.372 =$ _____

9. Round off 68,398 to the nearest thousand. _____

10. Round off 68.57894 to the nearest one. _____

11. $793 \times .46 =$ _____

The ancient Romans had a completely different number system from the one we use. *Roman numerals* are not used very much now. You sometimes see them in movie titles and on library walls. They can be fun to learn, rather like a secret code.

Here are the basic symbols that make up the numerals in the Roman system.

I = 1	L = 50	D = 500
V = 5	C = 100	M = 1000
X = 10		

Many other numbers are written by arranging Roman symbols from the highest value to the lowest, left to right, and then adding. When you do this you must remember *Rule 1: Never use the same symbol more than three times in a row.*

Examples:

XI = 11   (10 + 1)
XXII = 22   (10 + 10 + 1 + 1)
LXVIII = 68   (50 + 10 + 5 + 1 + 1 + 1)
MMCXXXV = 2,135 (1000 + 1000 + 100 + 10 + 10 + 10 + 5)

Write the following Roman numerals in our system of numbers. (Ours are called *Arabic numbers*.)

1. XIII ___13___
2. LXX ___70___
3. III ___3___
4. VI ___9___
5. VIII ___7___
6. XV ___15___
7. XXXI ___31___
8. LXII ___62___
9. LXXX ___80___
10. CC ___2000___
11. CXXX ___130___
12. DCC ___700___
13. CCXXVI ___226___

Now write the following Arabic numbers in Roman numerals.

14. 12 ___XII___
15. 25 ___XXV___
16. 33 ___XXXIII___
17. 26 ___XXVI___
18. 38 ___XXXVIII___
19. 63 ___LXIII___
20. 120 ___CXX___
21. 232 ___CCXXXII___
22. 358 ___CCCLVIII___
23. 523 ___DXXIII___
24. 700 ___DCC___
25. 835 ___DCCCXXXV___
26. 888 ___DCCCLXXXVIII___

Roman Numerals 2

Here again are the basic symbols that make up the numerals in the Roman system.

I = 1   L = 50   D = 500
V = 5   C = 100   M = 1000
X = 10

Remember that other numbers are written by arranging Roman symbols from the highest value to the lowest, left to right, and then adding. Remember *Rule 1: Never use the same symbol more than three times in a row.*

Write the following Roman numerals in our system of numbers. (Arabic numbers).

1. XXXVI _____

2. LXVII _____

3. CCXV _____

4. CCCXXI _____

5. DCCC _____

6. DCLV _____

7. MCCXXII _____

8. MMMCCCXXVIII _3328_
3000 +300 +28

Write the following Arabic numbers in Roman numerals.

9. 15 _____

10. 23 _____

11. 56 _____

12. 58 _____

13. 63 _____

14. 86 _____

15. 125 _____

16. 223 _____

17. 520 _____

18. 650 _____

19. 821 _____

20. 1,200 _____

21. 3,500 _MMMD_ _____

When a symbol for a smaller value appears in front of a larger one, subtract the symbol on the left from the one on its right. *Only certain symbols may be used to subtract. These are I, X, and C.*

Examples:

    IV = 4 (5 – 1) not IIII (Remember Rule 1.)
    IX = 9 (10 – 1)
    XL = 40 (50 – 10)
    CM = 900 (1000 – 100)
    95 = XCV not VC (Only I, X, C may be used to subtract.)

When you write Roman numerals where you must subtract the one on the left from the one on the right, you must remember *Rule 2: Subtract one symbol from the next highest symbol.*

Example:

    490 = CDXC (500 – 100) + (100 – 10)
    not
    XD which breaks Rule 2.

Here is a longer list of Roman numerals.

I	= 1	V	= 5	IX	= 9	XIII	= 13	XVII	= 17
II	= 2	VI	= 6	X	= 10	XIV	= 14	XVIII	= 18
III	= 3	VII	= 7	XI	= 11	XV	= 15	XIX	= 19
IV	= 4	VIII	= 8	XII	= 12	XVI	= 16	XX	= 20

Write the following Roman numerals in our numbers.

22. XLV _____

23. XXIX _____

24. XC _____

25. CD _____

Write the following numbers as Roman numerals.

26. 432 _____

27. 45 _____

28. 903 _____

29. 54 _____

30. 39 _____

1. $8.35 \times 2.3 =$ _____

2. $30.9 \times 634 =$ _____

3. $238 \times .64 =$ _____

4. A woman makes $7.55 an hour. How much can she make working for 9 hours?

   _____

5. The gas tank in Mr. Hamhock's car was empty. He filled it with gasoline that cost $1.36 a gallon. If the tank holds 15 gallons, how much did the fill-up cost?

   _____

6. A train goes 876 miles in 6 hours. How fast is the train going?

   _____

7. If 3 used paperback books cost 33 cents ($.33), how much will five books cost?

   _____

Find the interval, and then figure out what _A_ is in the following number line.

8.
```
   21          A          49
   |----|----|----|----|----|
```

   A = _____

9. Write 12,000,000 in words.

   _____

10. Write seven hundred forty billion in numbers.

    _____

11. Factors of 90 = _____

    _____

12. $21664 \div 9 =$ _____

13. Find the average of 19, 23, 18, 14, and 6.

    _____

14. Write 6.9 in words.

    _____

15. Write fourteen and twelve hundredths in numbers.

    _____

16. $69.47 + 24 + 1.993 =$ _____

17. $38.4 - 19.375 =$ _____

Round off the following numbers to the nearest million.

18. 42,674,214 _____

19. 607,218,999 _____

Round off the following decimal fractions to the nearest tenth.

20. .7734 _____

21. .9173 _____

Round off the following numbers to the nearest one.

22. 44.63321 _____

23. 501.19975 _____

24. 459.72231 _____

Remember:

Rule 1: Never use the same symbol more than three times in a row;
Rule 2: Subtract one symbol from the next highest symbol.

Write the following Roman numerals in Arabic numbers (our numbers). An asterisk (*) means that you must use subtraction to figure out the answer.

1. I _____

2. V _____

3. X _____

4. L _____

5. C _____

6. D _____

7. M _____

8. XXVII _____

9. LXVIII _____

10. LXXX _____

11. CXI _____

12. DCCCXV _____

13. DCI _____

14. CD* _____

15. CM* _____

16. CCXXIX* _____

17. MMDCCXIII _____

18. MCDXXII* _____

19. LXXIV* _____

20. CMLXIX* _____

21. MMMDCCCLXXXVIII _____

Write the following numbers in Roman numerals. An asterisk (*) means that you must use subtraction by putting a letter worth less in front of a letter worth more.

22. 27 _____

23. 83 _____

24. 90* _____

25. 43* _____

26. 44* _____

27. 49* _____

28. 61 _____

29. 128 _____

30. 248* _____

31. 401* _____

32. 557 _____

33. 724* _____

34. 1,328 _____

35. 3,215 _____

Answer the following questions using Arabic numbers.

36. At the end of a film, its date was stated as MCMXXXVIII. What year would that be?

_____

37. The title page of a book says the book was published in MDCCCLIV. What year was that?

_____

38. Printed on the back of a record album is the date MCMLXVII. In what year was the album recorded?

_____

Roman Numerals 4

Remember:

Rule 1: Never use the same symbol more than three times in a row;
Rule 2: Subtract one symbol from the next highest symbol.

Write the following Roman numerals in Arabic numbers (our numbers). An asterisk (*) means that you must use subtraction to figure out the answer.

1. I _____
2. V _____
3. X _____
4. L _____
5. C _____
6. D _____
7. M _____
8. XXI _____
9. XLIII* _____
10. XXIX* _____
11. LXXVI _____
12. LXXXIV* _84_____
13. CCXIII _____
14. CCCXXVII _____
15. DCCXX _____
16. CDLXXVI* _474_____
17. DCCCI _____
18. MDCCXXVIII _____
19. MMMCXXIII _____
20. CMXLIII* _____
21. CMXCIV* _____

Write the following Arabic numbers in Roman numerals. An asterisk (*) means that you must use subtraction by putting a letter worth less in front of a letter worth more.

22. 35 _____
23. 83 _____
24. 51 _____
25. 45* _____
26. 88 _____
27. 189* _____
28. 134* _____
29. 555 _____
30. 389* _____
31. 637 _____
32. 874* _____
33. 1,231 _____
34. 1,573 _____
35. 1,840* _____
36. 3,429* _____

Answer the next two questions using Arabic numbers.

37. A Roman grave has two dates, CLXIII–CCXLI, carved on its tombstone. When was the buried person born, and when did he or she die?

_____

38. Carved on the wall of a public library are the letters MDCCCXXXII. These tell when the library was built. In what year was it built?

_____

Write the following Roman numerals in Arabic numbers (our numbers).

1. XXVI _____

2. LXIII _____

3. XLVIII _____

4. CXVII _____

5. XC _____

6. CCCLXIII _____

7. CDXXVI _____

8. CMXXIV _____

9. MMCCCXV _____

10. MCMXXIX _____

11. MMMDCCLXXXVIII _____

Write the following Arabic numbers in Roman numerals.

12. 37 _____

13. 41 _____

14. 83 _____

15. 125 _____

16. 248 _____

17. 329 _____

18. 501 _____

19. 733 _____

20. 1,738 _____

21. 3,949 _____

22. 2,515 _____

Solve the following problems.

23. At the end of a film, the credits listed the date the film was made as MCMXXIII. What year was this? Answer in Arabic numbers.

    _____

24. An old book shows the publication date in the Roman numerals MDCCXIX. When was the book made? Answer in Arabic numbers.

    _____

25. Write the present year in Roman numerals.

    _____

1. Find the interval, and then figure out what *A* is on the following number line.

   18   A   33

   A = _____

2. Write 20,000,000,000,000 in words. _____

   Write six hundred eighty-five million in numbers. _____

3. Factor 60 three ways. _____ _____ _____

4. 41658 ÷ 8 = _____

5. Find the average of 356, 294, and 400. _____

6. Write 7.15 in words. _____

   Write nine and six thousandths in decimals. _____

7. 350.8 + 91.65 + 31 = _____

8. 26.5 − 3.416 = _____

9. Round off 79,346,299 to the nearest million. _____

10. Round off .6438691 to the nearest thousandth. _____

11. 620.7 × .56 = _____

In all of the following problems the divisor is 23. Work out the times table for 23 first; then do the division. Follow the same four steps you use in one-number division (divide, multiply, subtract, bring down). There will not be any remainders in these problems.

23 × 1 = ___23___

23 × 2 = ___46___

23 × 3 = ___69___

23 × 4 = ___92___

23 × 5 = _____

23 × 6 = _____

23 × 7 = _____

23 × 8 = _____

23 × 9 = _____

Example:

```
              5 94
        23 ) 136 62
             115 ↓↓
              21 6
              20 7 ↓
                 92
                 92
```

1.
```
   23 ) 8326
```

2.
```
   23 ) 16514
```

3.
```
   23 ) 13915
```

Use two-number division to do the following problems.

4. A boat took 23 hours to make a trip of 805 miles. How far did the boat travel each hour?

_____

5. A man made $15,732 in 23 weeks of work. How much did he make each week?

_____

6. A teacher bought 1,495 bags of potato chips. If he split them up evenly among the 23 students in his class, how many bags would each student get?

_____

First work out the times table chart for 47; then do the division. There will not be any remainders in these problems.

$47 \times 1 = \underline{\hspace{2cm}}$

$47 \times 2 = \underline{\hspace{2cm}}$

$47 \times 3 = \underline{\hspace{2cm}}$

$47 \times 4 = \underline{\hspace{2cm}}$

$47 \times 5 = \underline{\hspace{2cm}}$

$47 \times 6 = \underline{\hspace{2cm}}$

$47 \times 7 = \underline{\hspace{2cm}}$

$47 \times 8 = \underline{\hspace{2cm}}$

$47 \times 9 = \underline{\hspace{2cm}}$

1. $47 \overline{)31584}$

2. $47 \overline{)16873}$

3. $47 \overline{)37788}$

4. $47 \overline{)7849}$

5. $47 \overline{)101708}$

Use two-number division to do the following word problems.

6. During a race, a woman's heart beats 6,298 times in 47 minutes. How many times does her heart beat each minute?

   _____

7. A man worked 47 weeks of the year and made $11,656. How much did he make each week?

   _____

Write the following Roman numerals in Arabic numbers (our numbers).

1. DCCCLXVII _____

2. MMDCXLII _____

3. CMXXIV _____

4. MMCDLXXXIX _____

5. MMDCCXLVIII_____

Write the following Arabic numbers in Roman numerals.

6. 2,334 _____

7. 1,927 _____

8. 1,671_____

9. 3,425 _____

10. 3,888 _____

Find the interval, and then figure out what *A* is on the following number line.

11.
```
20            A      40
|__|__|__|__|__|__|
```

A = _____

12. Write 77,000,000 in words.

_____

13. Write nine hundred trillion in numbers.

_____

14. Factors of 77 = _____

15. 54222 ÷ 9 = _____

16. Find the average of 73, 18, and 41.

_____

17. Write 9.07 in words.

_____

18. Write seventeen and twelve thousandths in decimals.

_____

19. 77.9 + 2.037 = _____

20. 39.5 − 16.432 = _____

21. Round off 78,498 to the nearest thousand.

_____

Round off the following to the nearest hundredth.

22. .47938_____

23. .54301 _____

Round off the following to the nearest one.

24. 79.64 _____

25. 26.499_____

26. 83.5 × .19 _____

27. 742 × 1.57 = _____

28. Mr. Hogg walks into a restaurant and orders a bowl of clam chowder ($3.35), a shrimp cocktail ($5.25), a large medium-rare steak ($11.50), a side order of onion rings ($2.00), a plate of broccoli ($1.25), two glasses of lemonade ($ .95 each), and a hot fudge sundae ($2.25). What is his bill without the tip?

_____

29. A Roman gravestone says that the person buried under it lived from the year CCCXLVII to the year CDXXXVIII. How long did the person live? Answer in Arabic numbers.

_____

30. A tire dealer charged Mrs. Lenn $240 for a set of 5 new tires. How much did each tire cost?

_____

Make a times table for 56 if you need to. Then do the following division problems.

56 × 1 = _____

56 × 2 = _____

56 × 3 = _____

56 × 4 = _____

56 × 5 = _____

56 × 6 = _____

56 × 7 = _____

56 × 8 = _____

56 × 9 = _____

1. 56)‾27552‾

2. 56)‾39480‾

3. 56)‾3528‾

Make a times table for 39 if you need to. Then do the following division problems.

39 × 1 = _____

39 × 2 = _____

4. 39)‾33228‾

5. 39)‾5694‾

6. 39)‾37557‾

Use two-number division to solve the next two problems.

7. Juan saved the same amount of money each year. After 56 years he had $14,840. How much did he save each year?

_____

8. There are 52 weeks in a year. Lisa saved $12,168 last year. How much did she save each week?

_____

96

Two-Number Division 4

Make a times table for 36 if you need to. Then do the following division problems.

1.
$$36 \overline{)23220}$$

2.
$$36 \overline{)33732}$$

3.
$$36 \overline{)28908}$$

Make a times table for 52 if you need to. Then do the following division problems.

4.
$$52 \overline{)9672}$$

5.
$$52 \overline{)35568}$$

6.
$$52 \overline{)39312}$$

Do the next two division problems.

7. Matthew bought a computer and paid for it in 36 monthly payments. In all, the payments added up to $3,708. How much was each payment?

_____

8. A car traveled 205,920 feet in 39 minutes. How many feet did it go each minute?

_____

Do you know how many miles this is?

_____

97

Solve the following division problems. There will be no remainders in these problems.

1. 48) 35280

2. 48) 28992

3. 82) 13694

4. 82) 380398

Solve the following word problem.

5. A cross-country train went at an average speed of 82 miles an hour and covered 1,230 miles. How long did it take the train to go that far?

    _____

1. Find the interval, and then figure out what A is on the following number line.

14   A   49 $A =$ _____

2. Write 902,000,000,000 in words. _____

   Write fifty-three million in numbers. _____

3. Factor 55. _____

4. 42189 ÷ 7 = _____

5. Find the average of 60, 89, 54, 22, and 30. _____

6. Write 4.3 in words. _____

   Write nine and fifteen thousandths in decimals. _____

7. 49.5 + 3.862 + 31 = _____

8. 28.6 − 14.428 = _____

9. Round off 34,728,291 to the nearest million. _____

10. Round off .6439417 to the nearest tenth. _____

11. 20.9 × .47 = _____

12. Write MMDCCLXII in Arabic numbers. _____

    Write 3,428 in Roman numerals. _____

one millimeter = the width of this line ▬

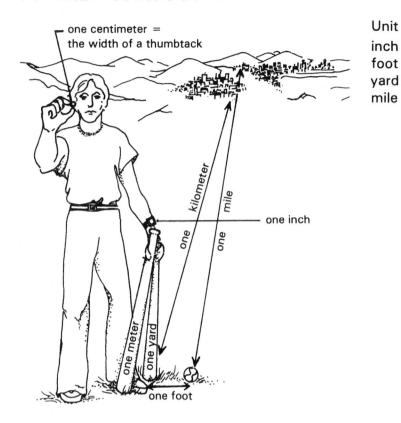

DISTANCE

English		Metric	
Unit	Abbreviation	Unit	Abbreviation
inch	in	millimeter	mm
foot	ft	centimeter	cm
yard	yd	meter	m
mile	mi	kilometer	km

Choose the best measure for each item below. Circle your choices in the English system and then in the metric system.

		English			Metric		
1.	Length of a new pencil.	in	ft	mi	cm	m	km
2.	Distance from the earth to the moon.	ft	yd	mi	mm	m	km
3.	Length of a book.	in	ft	yd	cm	m	km
4.	Length of your shoe.	in	yd	mi	mm	cm	m
5.	Length of your desk.	in	ft	mi	cm	m	km
6.	Length of a fingernail.	in	yd	mi	mm	m	km
7.	Length of a key.	2 in	2 ft	2 mi	50 mm	50 cm	50 m
8.	Length of a baseball bat.	3 in	3 ft	3 yd	1 cm	1 m	1 km
9.	Distance from New York to Chicago.	1000 ft		1000 mi	1600 cm		1600 km
10.	Length of a paper clip.	1 in	1 ft	1 yd	2 mm	2 cm	2 m
11.	Length of a football field.	100 in		100 yd	90 cm		90 m
12.	Length of your dictionary.	10 in	10 ft	10 yd	25 mm	25 cm	25m

VOLUME (Liquids)

English		Metric	
Unit	Abbreviations	Unit	Abbreviations
fluid ounce	fl oz	milliliter	ml
cup	cup	liter	l
pint	pt		
quart	qt		
gallon	gal		

one cup = 8 fl oz

one pint

one quart

one gallon

one milliliter = 1/5 teaspoon

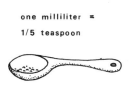

one liter

Choose the best measure for each item below. Circle your choices in the English system and then in the metric system.

		English			Metric	
1.	Volume of water in a bathtub.	cup	pt	gal	ml	l
2.	Volume of coffee in a coffee cup.	oz	cup	gal	ml	l
3.	Volume of gas in a gas tank.	pt	qt	gal	ml	l
4.	Volume of water in a raindrop.	oz	pt	qt	ml	l
5.	Volume of water in an ocean.	oz	qt	gal	ml	l
6.	Volume of a spoon.	1 oz		1 cup	6 ml	6 l
7.	Volume of soda in a soda bottle.	16 oz		16 gal	500 ml	500 l
8.	Volume of water in a fish tank.	20 cups		20 gals	80 ml	80 l
9.	Volume of water in a drinking glass.	8 oz		8 qt	240 ml	240 l

On the chart to the right, fill in the best measures for each item below. Use the English system and the metric system.

		English	Metric
10.	Volume of milk in a cat's dish.	_____	_____
11.	Volume of water in a river.	_____	_____
12.	Volume of chicken noodle soup in a can.	_____	_____
13.	Length of a highway.	_____	_____
14.	Volume of liquid in a test tube.	_____	_____
15.	Volume of water in a wading pool.	_____	_____
16.	Length of your classroom.	_____	_____
17.	Volume of orange juice in an orange.	_____	_____

Review 15

Work out a times table chart for 53 and use it to solve the following division problems.

53 × 1 = _____

53 × 2 = _____

53 × 3 = _____

53 × 4 = _____

53 × 5 = _____

53 × 6 = _____

53 × 7 = _____

53 × 8 = _____

53 × 9 = _____

1. 19716 ÷ 53 = _____

2. 43248 ÷ 53 = _____

3. 21677 ÷ 53 = _____

4. 3432 ÷ 143 = _____

5. Write 704,000,000 in words.

_____

_____

6. Write ninety-one trillion in numbers.

_____

7. Write 16.004 in words.

_____

_____

8. Write twelve and seventeen hundredths in numbers.

_____

9. Factors of 34 = _____

10. Find the average of 100, 200, and 306.

11. 9.793 + 16.4 + 35 = _____

12. 38.4 − 13.159 = _____

13. Round off 708,543 to the nearest thousand.

_____

14. Round off .773491 to the nearest thousandth.

_____

15. Round off 73.9931 to the nearest one.

_____

16. 21.8 × 3.7 = _____

17. Write MMDCCCXLVI in Arabic numbers.

_____

18. Write 3,438 in Roman numerals.

_____

19. Harvey sees that a library was built in MDCCCXCIII — that's the way the date is carved on the front of the building. What year was that? Answer in Arabic numbers.

_____

20. A supersonic airliner traveled 5,808 miles in 4 hours. How far did it travel each hour?

_____

21. How far can the same plane travel in 3 hours at the same speed?

_____

22. A man who weighs 208 pounds hears that he would weigh much less on the moon because the moon's gravity isn't as strong as ours. He finds out that his weight on the moon would be .17 of what it is on earth. How much would he weigh on the moon?

23. A runner is puffing around a track training for a big race. His heart is beating 119 times a minute. If he keeps running for 55 minutes, how many times will his heart beat during that time?

WEIGHT

English		Metric	
Unit	Abbreviation	Unit	Abbreviation
ounce	oz	milligram	mg
pound	lb	gram	g
ton	tn	kilogram	kg

one ounce

one ton

one milligram = one small eyelash

one gram

one kilogram

COFFEE

one pound

CANDY

SUGAR

Choose the best measure for each item below. Circle your choices in the English system and then in the metric system.

		English			Metric		
1.	Weight of a car.	oz	lb	tn	mg	g	kg
2.	Weight of a paper clip.	oz	lb	tn	mg	g	kg
3.	Weight of a twelve-year-old boy.	oz	lb	tn	mg	g	kg
4.	Weight of a fly.	oz	lb	tn	mg	g	kg
5.	Weight of a dog.	oz	lb	tn	mg	g	kg
6.	Weight of a bicycle.		25 lb	25 tn		12 g	12 kg
7.	Weight of an adult woman.	130 oz	130 lb		59 mg		59 kg
8.	Weight of a ruler.	1 oz	1 lb		30 mg	30 g	

		English			Metric		
9.	Weight of a person.	mi	in	lb	m	g	kg
10.	Volume of water in a raindrop.	oz	in	tn	kg	l	ml
11.	Weight of a house.	oz	in	tn	kg	l	ml
12.	Weight of a mosquito.	yd	cup	oz	km	mm	mg
13.	Length of your arm.	in	lb	qt	g	cm	km
14.	Length of a desk.	tn	ft	gal	mg	cm	l
15.	Volume of milk in a carton.	lb	gal	ft	l	kg	mg
16.	Weight of a cow.	lb	gal	ft	l	kg	mg

DISTANCE

English		Metric	
Unit	Abbreviation	Unit	Abbreviation
ich	in	millimeter	mm
ot	ft	centimeter	cm
ard	yd	meter	m
ile	mi	kilometer	km

VOLUME (Liquids)

English		Metric	
Unit	Abbreviation	Unit	Abbreviation
fluidounce	fl oz	milliliter	ml
cup		liter	l
pint	pt		
quart	qt		
gallon	gal		

WEIGHT

English		Metric	
Unit	Abbreviation	Unit	Abbreviation
ounce	oz	milligram	mg
pound	lb	gram	g
ton	tn	kilogram	kg

hoose the best measure for each item below. Circle your choices in the English system and then the metric system.

	English			Metric		
1. Length of a car.	in	qt	yd	mm	m	kg
2. Volume of shampoo in a bottle.	gal	oz	lb	cm	g	ml
3. Diameter of a button.	oz	in	cup	mg	mm	ml
4. Weight of Earth.	qt	gal	tn	kg	km	g
5. Volume of juice in a can.	2 cups		12 cups	500 ml		500 l
6. Height of a tall tree.	22 in		22 yd	20 cm		20 m
7. Weight of a puppy.	2 lb		20 tn	l g		1 kg
8. Length of a basketball court.	25 ft		25 yd	30 cm		23 m

n the chart to the right, fill in the best measure for each item below. Use the English system and he metric system.

	English	Metric
9. Weight of an eyelash.	_____	_____
0. Volume of water in a pail.	_____	_____
1. Height of a skyscraper.	_____	_____
2. Volume of water in a melted popsicle.	_____	_____
3. Weight of a tractor.	_____	_____
4. Weight of a dish.	_____	_____
5. Length of a spoon.	_____	_____

Fill in the correct English and metric terms on the charts below. You will receive extra credit if you put the terms in order from smallest to biggest.

Choose your answers from the following list.

millimeter	inch	cup	foot	quart
ton	gram	ounce (weight)	milligram	pound
yard	kilometer	centimeter	mile	kilogram
pint	liter	milliliter	gallon	meter
				ounce (volume)

DISTANCE

English		Metric
1. _____		5. _____
2. _____		6. _____
3. _____		7. _____
4. _____		8. _____

VOLUME (Liquids)

English		Metric
9. _____		14. _____
10. _____		15. _____
11. _____		
12. _____		
13. _____		

WEIGHT

English		Metric
16. _____		19. _____
17. _____		20. _____
18. _____		21. _____

In the metric system, what would be the best measure for the following items?

22. The weight of a submarine. _____

23. The thickness of a dime. _____

In the English system, what would be the best measure for the following items?

24. The weight of a boy. _____

25. The distance to London. _____

26. The volume of water in a swimming pool. _____

Review Test 15

1. Find the interval, and then figure out what A is on the following number line.

   16   A   26

   $A =$ _____

2. Write 217,000 in words. _____

   Write forty-nine trillion in numbers. _____

3. Factor 50 two ways. _____   _____

4. 27250 ÷ 9 = _____

5. Find the average of 263 and 425. _____

6. Write 7.06 in words. _____

   Write fourteen and twelve thousandths in decimals. _____

7. 3.1 + 89 + 62.43 = _____

8. 64.5 − 29.173 = _____

9. Round off 67,289 to the nearest thousand. _____

10. Round off .4782941 to the nearest hundredth. _____

11. 9.67 × 4.83 = _____

12. Write MCMLXXVII in Arabic numbers. _____

    Write 2,674 in Roman numerals. _____

13. 8964 ÷ 36 = _____

Learn the following important facts.

Money

5 cents = 1 nickel
10 cents = 1 dime
25 cents = 1 quarter
50 cents = 1 half-dollar
100 cents = 1 dollar

Time

60 seconds = 1 minute
60 minutes = 1 hour
24 hours = 1 day
7 days = 1 week
365 days = 1 year
10 years = 1 decade
100 years = 1 century

Days in the Months

Thirty days have September,
April, June, and November.
All the rest have thirty-one,
Except February with
     twenty-eight,
And twenty-nine in a
     leap year.

Use the facts listed on the left to fill in answers on the following lines.

1. 1 day has __24__ hours, so 5 days have __120__ hours. (24 × 5 = 120)

2. 1 dollar has __100__ cents, so 4 dollars have _____ cents.

3. 1 decade has _____ years, so 6 decades have _____ years.

4. 1 year has _____ days, so 3 years have _____ days.

5. 1 quarter has _____ cents, so 6 quarters have _____ cents.

6. 1 dime has _____ cents, so 7 dimes have _____ cents.

7. 1 century has _____ years, so 3 centuries have _____ years.

8. 1 week has _____ days, so 5 weeks have _____ days.

9. How many days are in March? _____

10. How many days are in April? _____

11. How many days are in a week? _____

12. How many years are in a decade? _____

13. How many years are in a century? _____

14. How many days are in June? _____

Learn and remember the following important facts.

Distance

12 inches = 1 foot
3 feet = 1 yard
5,280 feet = 1 mile

Weight

16 ounces = 1 pound
2,000 pounds = 1 ton

Liquids

2 cups = 1 pint
2 pints = 1 quart
4 quarts = 1 gallon

Time

60 seconds = 1 minute
60 minutes = 1 hour
24 hours = 1 day
7 days = 1 week
365 days = 1 year
10 years = 1 decade
100 years = 1 century

Money

5 cents = 1 nickel
10 cents = 1 dime
25 cents = 1 quarter
50 cents = 1 half-dollar
100 cents = 1 dollar

Days in the Months

Thirty days have September,
April, June, and November.
All the rest have thirty-one,
Except February with
    twenty-eight,
And twenty-nine in a
    leap year.

Use the facts listed on the left to fill in answers on the following lines.

1. 1 pound has _____ ounces, so 7 pounds have _____ ounces.

2. 1 hour has _____ minutes, so 4 hours have _____ minutes.

3. 1 ton has _____ pounds, so 9 tons have _____ pounds.

4. 1 gallon has _____ quarts, so 10 gallons have _____ quarts.

5. 1 week has _____ days, so 5 weeks have _____ days.

6. 1 dollar has _____ cents, so 20 dollars have _____ cents.

7. 1 mile has _____ feet, so 3 miles have _____ feet.

8. 1 year has _____ days, so 5 years have _____ days.

9. 1 yard has _____ feet, so 300 yards have _____ feet.

10. 1 decade has _____ years, so 4 decades have _____ years.

11. How many days are in July? _____

12. How many days are in November? _____

13. How many days are in April? _____

14. How many days are in January? _____

15. How many days are in March? _____

16. How many days are in June? _____

17. How many days are in February in a leap year? _____

    In a non-leap year? _____

Review 16

Circle the best English and metric measure for the distance across the Atlantic Ocean.

1. inches
   feet
   yards
   miles

2. millimeters
   centimeters
   meters
   kilometers

Write the best English and metric measure for the length of your thumb.

3. _____   4. _____

Circle the best English and metric measure for the volume of milk in a small glass.

5. ounce
   cup
   pint
   quart
   gallon

6. milliliter
   liter

Write the best English and metric measure for the volume of water in a bathtub.

7. _____   8. _____

Circle the best English and metric measure for the weight of an ocean liner.

9. ounce
   pound
   ton

10. milligram
    gram
    kilogram

Write the best English and metric measure for the weight of a letter.

11. _____   12. _____

13. Write 407,000,000,000 in words.

_____

_____

14. Write ninety-four trillion in numbers.

_____

15. Find the interval, and then figure out what *A* is on the following number line.

14 | | | | | A   49

A = _____

16. Factors of 99 = _____

17. Find the average of 97, 14, 28, and 53.

_____

18. Write 3.05 in words.

_____

_____

19. Write sixteen and twelve thousandths in decimals.

_____

20. $29 + 3.59 =$ _____

21. $36.4 - 29.177 =$ _____

22. Round off 78,342,799,418 to the nearest billion.

_____

23. Round off .777431 to the nearest hundredth.

_____

24. Round off 17.83 to the nearest one.

_____

25. Round off 98.15 to the nearest one.

_____

26. $45.3 \times 1.8 =$ _____

27. Write MMCDLXVII in Arabic numbers.

_____

28. Write 3,449 in Roman numerals.

_____

29. $15043 \div 49 =$ _____

30. $26411 \div 49 =$ _____

31. Sylvia had $198.73 in her checking account in the bank. She wrote a check for $38.69 for a coat. How much was left in the bank?

32. Anna the Wizard took four math tests and got the following grades: 94, 87, 95, and 92. What was her average for these tests?

Remember the following facts.

Distance
12 inches = 1 foot
3 feet = 1 yard
5,280 feet = 1 mile

Weight
16 ounces = 1 pound
2,000 pounds = 1 ton

Liquids
2 cups = 1 pint
2 pints = 1 quart
4 quarts = 1 gallon

Time
60 seconds = 1 minute
60 minutes = 1 hour
24 hours = 1 day
7 days = 1 week
365 days = 1 year
10 years = 1 decade
100 years = 1 century

Money
5 cents = 1 nickel
10 cents = 1 dime
25 cents = 1 quarter
50 cents = 1 half-dollar
100 cents = 1 dollar

Days in the Months
Thirty days have September,
April, June, and November.
All the rest have thirty-one,
Except February with
    twenty-eight,
And twenty-nine in a
    leap year.

Answer the following questions. On the first fifteen you will have to divide.

1. How many hours are in 180 minutes? _____

2. How many quarters are in 75 cents? _____

3. How many gallons are in 20 quarts? _____

4. How many pounds are in 64 ounces? _____

5. How many days are in 48 hours? _____

6. How many weeks are in 42 days? _____

7. How many miles are in 31,680 feet? _____

8. How many feet are in 60 inches? _____

9. How many dimes are in 40 cents? _____

10. How many pints are in 16 cups? _____

11. How many yards are in 27 feet? _____

12. How many tons are in 14,000 pounds? _____

13. How many years are in 730 days? _____

14. How many minutes are in 300 seconds? _____

15. How many nickels are in 90 cents? _____

16. How many days are in April? _____

17. How many days are in December? _____

18. How many days are in June? _____

19. How many days are in May? _____

20. How many days are in July? _____

Fill in the correct answers.

21. 10 days = _____ week and _____ days.

22. 19 ounces = _____ pound and _____ ounces.

23. 113 cents = _____ dollar and _____ cents.

24. 72 minutes = _____ hour and _____ minutes.

25. 23 days = _____ weeks and _____ days.

Fill in the correct answers on the following lines to complete the facts.

Distance

1. ____ inches = 1 foot
2. ____ feet = 1 yard
3. ____ feet = 1 mile

Weight

4. ____ ounces = 1 pound
5. ____ pounds = 1 ton

Liquids

6. ____ cups = 1 pint
7. ____ pints = 1 quart
8. ____ quarts = 1 gallon

Time

9. ____ seconds = 1 minute
10. ____ minutes = 1 hour
11. ____ hours = 1 day
12. ____ days = 1 week
13. ____ days = 1 year
14. ____ years = 1 decade
15. ____ years = 1 century

Money

16. ____ cents = 1 nickel
17. ____ cents = 1 dime
18. ____ cents = 1 quarter
19. ____ cents = 1 half-dollar
20. ____ cents = 1 dollar

Days in the Months

21. ____ days have
September,
April, June, and
November.
All the rest have ____,
Except February with
____,
And ____ in a leap year.

Answer the following questions. Be careful; some call for multiplication and others for division.

22. How many pounds in 8 tons? _____
23. How many quarts are in 6 pints? _____
24. How many feet are in 5 yards? _____
25. How many centuries are in 500 years? _____
26. How many dimes are in 60 cents? _____
27. How many cups are in 2 pints? _____
28. How many days are in 3 years? _____
29. How many feet are in 6 miles? _____
30. How many pounds are in 160 ounces? _____
31. How many years are in 2 decades? _____
32. How many minutes are in 240 seconds? _____
33. How many days are in 8 years? _____
34. How many weeks are in 28 days? _____
35. How many minutes are in 6 hours? _____
36. How many minutes are in 3 hours? _____
37. How many feet are in 84 inches? _____
38. How many days are in November? _____
39. How many days are in August? _____
40. How many days are in September? _____
41. How many days are in a non-leap year February? _____

Fill in the correct answers.

42. 9 quarts = _____ gallons and _____ quart.
43. 49 hours = _____ days and _____ hour.
44. 213 cents = _____ dollars and _____ cents.
45. 29 days = _____ weeks and _____ day.
46. 428 years = _____ centuries, _____ decades, _____ years.
47. 400 days = _____ year and _____ days.

Fill in the following lines to complete the facts.

1. _____ inches = 1 foot

2. _____ feet = 1 yard

3. _____ feet = 1 mile

4. _____ ounces = 1 pound

5. _____ pounds = 1 ton

6. _____ cups = 1 pint

7. _____ pints = 1 quart

8. _____ quarts = 1 gallon

9. _____ seconds = 1 minute

10. _____ minutes = 1 hour

11. _____ hours = 1 day

12. _____ days = 1 week

13. _____ days = 1 year

14. _____ years = 1 decade

15. _____ years = 1 century

16. _____ cents = 1 nickel

17. _____ cents = 1 dime

18. _____ cents = 1 quarter

19. _____ cents = 1 half-dollar

20. _____ cents = 1 dollar

21. _____ days, have September
April, June, and November.

All the rest have _____.

Except February with _____

And _____ in a leap year.

Now answer the following questions.

22. How many pounds are in 3 tons? _____

23. How many cents are in 5 dollars? _____

24. How many ounces are in 4 pounds? _____

25. How many cents are in 7 nickels? _____

26. How many feet are in 10 yards? _____

27. How many pounds are in 6 tons? _____

28. How many pints are in 4 quarts? _____

29. How many minutes are in 5 hours? _____

30. How many days are in 9 weeks? _____

31. How many inches are in 8 feet? _____

32. How many feet are in 4 miles? _____

33. How many seconds are in 3 minutes? _____

34. How many days are in 5 years? _____

35. How many cents are in 5 quarters? _____

36. How many years are in 8 centuries? _____

37. How many quarts are in 18 gallons? _____

38. How many days are in November? _____

39. How many days are in January? _____

40. How many days are in March? _____

41. How many days are in June? _____

Fill in the correct answers.

42. 12 days = _____ week and _____ days.

43. 212 cents = _____ dollars and _____ cents.

44. 600 days = _____ year and _____ days.

45. 9 quarts = _____ gallons and _____ quart.

46. 50 hours = _____ days and _____ hours.

1. Find the interval, and then figure out what A is on the following number line.

A = _____

2. Write 97,000,000 in words. _____

   Write five hundred thousand in numbers. _____

3. Factor 40 three ways. _____   _____   _____

4. 49643 ÷ 8 = _____

5. Find the average of 7, 9, and 5. _____

6. Write 12.017 in words. _____

   Write four and one hundredth in decimals. _____

7. 680 + 29.6 = _____

8. 21.4 − 6.289 = _____

9. Round off 26,549,342,015 to the nearest billion. _____

10. Round off 49.3789218 to the nearest one. _____

11. 8.06 × 26 = _____

12. Write MMMDCXLIII in Arabic numbers. _____

    Write 2,368 in Roman numerals. _____

13. 9716 ÷ 28 = _____

When you divide decimals, follow these steps:

1) Move the decimal point over to the right side of the divisor.
2) Move the decimal point over the same number of places to the right in the dividend.
3) In the answer, put the decimal point straight above the place where it is in the dividend.
4) Divide.

$$.45.\overline{)1.03.5}\text{ dividend}$$
2 places   2 places

Put the decimal points in the correct places in each answer below.

1.
$$\begin{array}{r} 75\ 1 \\ .38.\overline{)28.53.8} \end{array}$$
2 places   2 places

2.
$$\begin{array}{r} 8\ 06 \\ 2.9\overline{)233.74} \end{array}$$

3.
$$\begin{array}{r} 243 \\ .7\overline{).1701} \end{array}$$

4.
$$\begin{array}{r} 642 \\ .013\overline{).8346} \end{array}$$

5.
$$\begin{array}{r} 8\ 64 \\ .9\overline{)77.76} \end{array}$$

6.
$$\begin{array}{r} 374 \\ 3.64\overline{)13.6136} \end{array}$$

Now work out the following problems. Be sure to put the decimal points in the correct places.

7.
$$.5\overline{)3.640}$$

8.
$$.7\overline{)44.94}$$

9.
$$.6\overline{)34.32}$$

10.
$$.3\overline{).2853}$$

11.
$$.7\overline{).413}$$

12.
$$.8\overline{)29.6}$$

13.
$$.4\overline{)3.32}$$

14.
$$.9\overline{).333}$$

Division of Decimals 2

Put the decimal points in the correct places in the following answers.

1.
$$2.6 \overline{)1.7706} \quad 681$$

2.
$$.05 \overline{).3420} \quad 684$$

3.
$$.31 \overline{)21.204} \quad 684$$

4.
$$.541 \overline{)1.91514} \quad 354$$

5.
$$.007 \overline{).5894} \quad 842$$

6.
$$.00235 \overline{)1.97870} \quad 842$$

Now work out the following problems. Be sure to put the decimal points in the correct places.

7.
$$.6 \overline{)5.118}$$

8.
$$.5 \overline{)22.15}$$

9.
$$.7 \overline{)213.5}$$

10.
$$.9 \overline{)6.777}$$

11.
$$.27 \overline{)1.8144}$$

12.
$$2.7 \overline{)123.93}$$

1. Circle the best metric measure for your weight.

   milligrams
   grams
   kilograms

2. Circle the best metric measure for the length of your foot.

   millimeter
   centimeter
   meter
   kilometer

3. Circle the best metric measure for a spoonful of medicine.

   milliliter
   liter

4. How many inches are in a foot? _____

5. How many feet are in a yard? _____

6. How many feet are in a mile? _____

7. How many ounces are in a pound? _____

8. How many pounds are in a ton? _____

9. How many cups are in a pint? _____

10. How many pints are in a quart? _____

11. How many quarts are in a gallon? _____

12. How many seconds are in a minute? _____

13. How many minutes are in an hour? _____

14. How many hours are in a day? _____

15. How many days are in a year? _____

16. How many days are in a leap year? _____

17. How many years are in a decade? _____

18. How many years are in a century? _____

19. How many days are in January? _____

20. How many days are in June? _____

21. How many days are in December? _____

22. How many days are in February

    in a leap year? _____

    in a non-leap year? _____

23. Find the interval, and then figure out what A is on the following number line.

    12   A   20

    A = _____

24. Write 305,000 in words.

    _____

    _____

25. Write two hundred trillion in numbers.

    _____

26. Factors of 42 = _____

27. Find the average of 41 and 37.

    _____

28. Write 16.002 in words.

    _____

    _____

29. Write five and eleven hundredths in decimals.

    _____

30. $78 + 4.908 =$ _____

31. $61.9 - 28.715 =$ _____

32. Round off 78,935 to the nearest thousand.

    _____

33. Round off 6.333333 to the nearest tenth.

    _____

34. Write MCDLXXX in Arabic numbers.

    _____

35. $42.3 \times .15 =$ _____

36. Write 3,933 in Roman numerals.

_____

37. Gloria and her best friend decide to take an 855 mile bicycle trip. They think they can go about 45 miles a day. About how long will the trip take?

_____

38. Mr. Gleason took his family to a restaurant to celebrate his wife's birthday.
Mr. Gleason's order came to $8.73, his wife's food came to $4.79, his son's order was $5.15, and his daughter's came to $9.05. What was the total bill?

_____

Division of Decimals 3

Put decimal points in the correct places in the following answers. You may have to add a zero to the beginning or end of some answers.

1.
$$.64 \overline{) 4819.2} \quad 75\ 3$$

2.
$$2.1 \overline{) 1.6947} \quad 807$$

3.
$$34.2 \overline{) 2.21958} \quad 649$$

In the following problems you don't have to move a decimal point in the divisor, so just bring the decimal point in the dividend straight up into the answer.

4.
$$7 \overline{) 47.95} \quad 6\ 85$$

5.
$$62 \overline{) 46.872} \quad 756$$

6.
$$9 \overline{) 757.8} \quad 84\ 2$$

7.
$$6 \overline{) 5.04} \quad 84$$

Now work out the following problems. Make sure you put decimal points in the correct places.

8.
$$.4 \overline{) 2.728}$$

9.
$$5 \overline{) 29.80}$$

10.
$$.07 \overline{) 459.9}$$

11.
$$2 \overline{) 3.8}$$

12.
$$.63 \overline{) 19.404}$$

13.
$$6.3 \overline{) 61.173}$$

Carefully work out the following problems. Make sure to put the decimal points in the correct places.

1.

$$.6 \overline{) 51.786}$$

2.

$$5 \overline{) 247.0}$$

3.

$$.07 \overline{) 4.081}$$

4.

$$.3 \overline{) 21.6}$$

5.

$$.37 \overline{) 9.879}$$

6.

$$.037 \overline{) 234.58}$$

Do the next two word problems.

7. A candy bar costs $ .56 (fifty-six cents). How many candy bars can a girl buy with $14.00?

_____

8. A teacher finds $46.25 and decides to divide the money evenly among the 37 students in his class. How much will each student get?

_____

Test 17 — Division of Decimals

Put the decimal point in the correct place in each answer.

1. $4.6\overline{)302.22}$ 6 57

2. $.04\overline{)3.364}$ 841

3. $.0149\overline{)5.215}$ 35

4. $8\overline{)30.72}$ 3 84

Now solve the following problems.

5. $.7\overline{)4.774}$

6. $5\overline{)381.5}$

7. $.006\overline{)25.56}$

8. $.43\overline{)15.093}$

9. $4.3\overline{)2.8896}$

Solve the word problem below.

10. At the school store, a pencil costs $.09 (nine cents). How many can you buy for $5.76?

_____

122

Review Test 17

1. Find the interval, and then figure out what A is on the following number line.

   48   A   58

   A = _____

2. Write 218,000,000,000,000 in words. _____

   Write nine hundred nine million in numbers. _____

3. Factor 35. _____

4. 36320 ÷ 6 = _____

5. What is the average of 87, 74, and 91? _____

6. Write 8.12 in words. _____

   Write fifteen and seven thousandths in decimals. _____

7. 42.96 + 2.147 = _____

8. 8.6 − 2.475 = _____

9. Round off 27,218 to the nearest thousand. _____

10. Round off .7777777 to the nearest hundredth. _____

11. 29.7 × 4.3 = _____

12. Write MMDCCCLXIX in Arabic numbers. _____

    Write 3,427 in Roman numerals. _____

13. 213.18 ÷ 3.4 = _____

Unit 18 — Graphing 1

This *line graph* shows the highest temperature in each of the 12 months of the year in one American city.

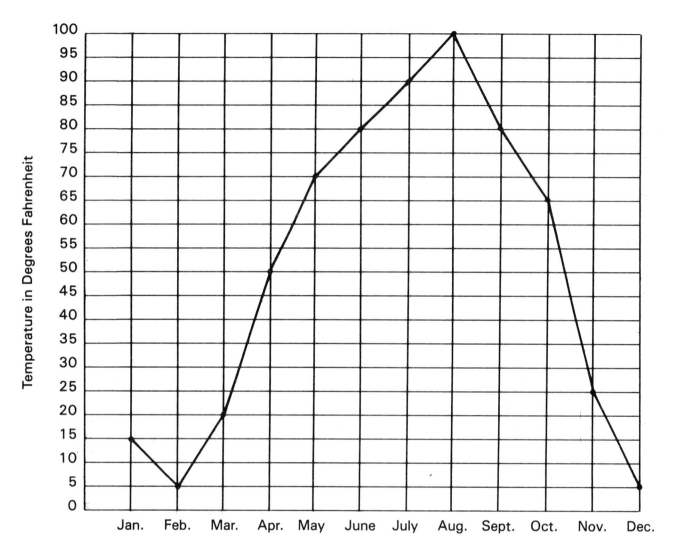

Use the graph above to answer the following questions.

1. What was the high temperature in May? _____

2. What were the two coldest months? _____ _____

3. What was the next-to-hottest month? _____

4. The biggest rise in temperature came after which month? _____

5. In which two months was the high temperature 80°? _____ _____

6. In which month was the high temperature 20°? _____

7. By looking at this graph, what could you say about the climate of this city? Would you want to live there? Why or why not?

    _____

    _____

Graphing 2

Make a line graph of a boy's spelling test scores during the year. The first three have been done for you.

Test 1	35%	Test 6	40%	Test 11	55%	Test 16	90%
Test 2	30%	Test 7	45%	Test 12	80%	Test 17	90%
Test 3	25%	Test 8	55%	Test 13	5%	Test 18	95%
Test 4	30%	Test 9	60%	Test 14	70%	Test 19	100%
Test 5	30%	Test 10	60%	Test 15	80%	Test 20	100%

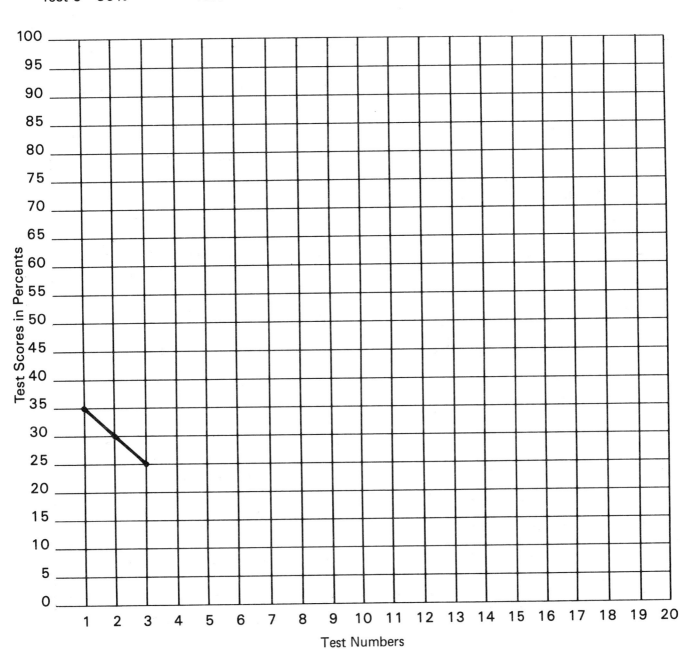

Work out a times table chart for 67 and use it to solve the following division problems.

67 × 1 = _____

67 × 2 = _____

67 × 3 = _____

67 × 4 = _____

67 × 5 = _____

67 × 6 = _____

67 × 7 = _____

67 × 8 = _____

67 × 9 = _____

1. 351.08 ÷ 6.7 = _____

2. .12931 ÷ .67 = _____

3. 27202 ÷ 6.7 = _____

4. 65.124 ÷ 67 = _____

5. How many days are in March? _____

6. How many days are in September? _____

7. How many pounds are in a ton? _____

8. How many days are in a non-leap year?

_____

9. How many ounces are in a pound? _____

10. How many minutes are in an hour? _____

11. How many quarts are in a gallon? _____

12. How many inches are in a foot? _____

13. Find the interval, and figure out what *A* is on the following number line.

18   A   42

A = _____

14. Write 419,000,000 in words.

_____

_____

15. Write seventeen billion in numbers.

_____

16. Factors of 18 = _____

17. Find the average of 35, 48, and 28.

_____

18. Write 19.003 in words.

_____

_____

19. Write two and nine tenths in decimals.

_____

20. 7.14 + 48.937 = _____

21. 63.5 − 21.731 = _____

22. Round off 67,922,318 to the nearest million.

_____

23. Round off .428472 to the nearest thousandth.

_____

24. Write MDC in Arabic numbers.

_____

25. Write MMLXXVII in Arabic numbers.

_____

26. Write 3,429 in Roman numerals.

_____

27. Shelley weighs 85 pounds. She hears that on Jupiter she would weigh 2.54 times as much because the gravity there is greater. How much would she weigh if she were standing on Jupiter?

28. At the beginning of an old book it says that it was published in the year MDCCLXXIX. What year was that?

Graphing 3

Make a *bar graph* of the number of people who think a make-believe president is doing a good job. Finish numbering the axes of the graph, and then form bars by using the information given below to darken areas on the graph. Note that the horizontal numbers (numbers running across) on a bar graph go in the spaces between the lines. The bar for the president's first month in office has been done for you.

Month 1	65%	Month 7	40%	Month 13	80%
Month 2	70%	Month 8	35%	Month 14	80%
Month 3	73%	Month 9	31%	Month 15	79%
Month 4	80%	Month 10	25%	Month 16	65%
Month 5	71%	Month 11	80%	Month 17	69%
Month 6	65%	Month 12	85%	Month 18	70%

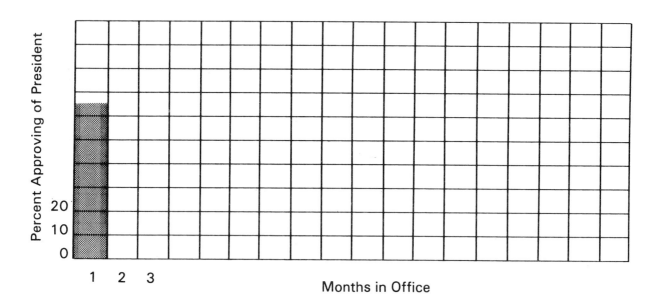

Use the graph above to answer the following questions.

1. In which month was the president most popular? _____

2. In which month was the president least popular? _____

3. In which month did 31% of the people approve of the president? _____

4. In which 2 months did 70% approve of the president? _____ _____

5. In which 4 months did the president have a big problem with popularity?

   _____ _____ _____ _____

6. In which month did the president win back support? _____

7. What did people think of this president over the 18 months? Describe the trend in popularity in your own words.

   _____

   _____

   _____

Graphing 4

Make a bar graph of the speed of a racing car given at one-minute intervals during a race. First, label the axes on the graph with the minutes running horizontally or across (one to each space) and the speeds running vertically or up and down (10 mph for each line). Then, form bars by darkening areas on the graph according to the information given below.

Minute 1	20 mph	Minute 8	20 mph	Minute 15	150 mph	Minute 22	50 mph
Minute 2	130 mph	Minute 9	100 mph	Minute 16	160 mph	Minute 23	50 mph
Minute 3	150 mph	Minute 10	100 mph	Minute 17	180 mph	Minute 24	75 mph
Minute 4	130 mph	Minute 11	90 mph	Minute 18	200 mph	Minute 25	90 mph
Minute 5	180 mph	Minute 12	95 mph	Minute 19	200 mph	Minute 26	150 mph
Minute 6	200 mph	Minute 13	130 mph	Minute 20	10 mph	Minute 27	190 mph
Minute 7	155 mph	Minute 14	140 mph	Minute 21	40 mph	Minute 28	200 mph

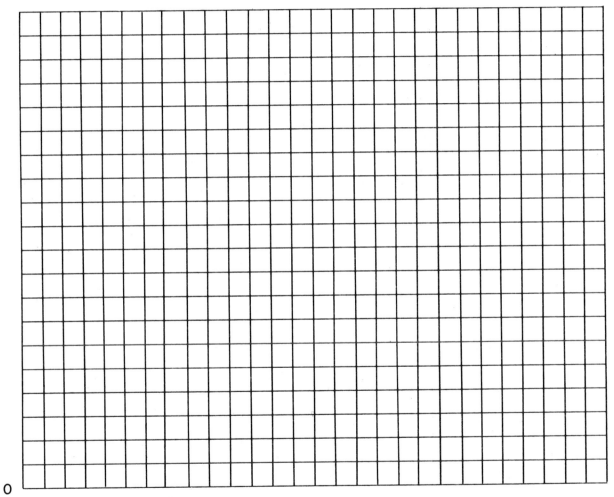

0

129

Make a line graph of the number of cars crossing a bridge during a 24-hour period. Label the axes on the graph with the hours running horizontally or across (one hour for each line) and the number of cars running vertically or up and down (5 cars for each line). Use the following information to make your graph.

Hour 1	5 Cars	Hour 7	90 Cars	Hour 13	60 Cars	Hour 19	75 Cars
Hour 2	5 Cars	Hour 8	100 Cars	Hour 14	60 Cars	Hour 20	40 Cars
Hour 3	0 Cars	Hour 9	96 Cars	Hour 15	50 Cars	Hour 21	31 Cars
Hour 4	10 Cars	Hour 10	80 Cars	Hour 16	89 Cars	Hour 22	13 Cars
Hour 5	25 Cars	Hour 11	50 Cars	Hour 17	90 Cars	Hour 23	10 Cars
Hour 6	50 Cars	Hour 12	47 Cars	Hour 18	100 Cars	Hour 24	2 Cars

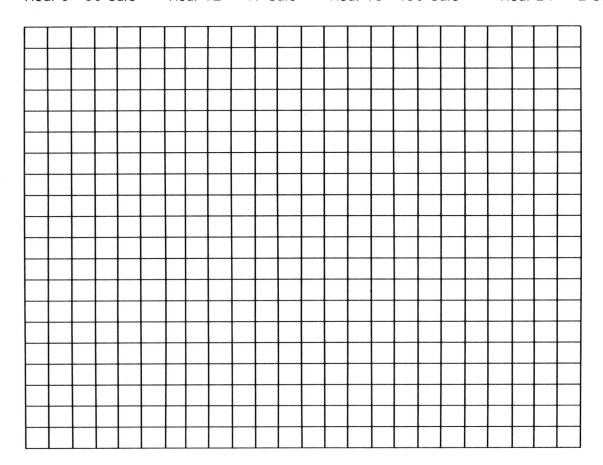

Use the line graph above to answer the following questions.

1. During which hour did the bridge have the heaviest traffic? _____

2. During which hour did the bridge have the lightest traffic? _____

3. How many cars crossed the bridge in hour 15? _____

4. In which two hours did 90 cars cross the bridge? _____ _____

5. Between which hours was there the sharpest increase in traffic? _____

6. What can you say about the traffic on this bridge over a 24-hour period? Where do you think the bridge is located? What else can you tell?

1. Find the interval, and then figure out what *A* is on the following number line.

27   A   34   A = _____

2. Write 501,000,000 in words. _____

   Write sixty trillion in numbers. _____

3. Factor 70 two ways. _____   _____

4. 74747 ÷ 9 = _____

5. Find the average of 268 and 490. _____

6. Write 4.2 in words. _____

   Write five and one hundredth in decimals. _____

7. 86 + 9.35 = _____

8. 24.7 − 15.473 = _____

9. Round off 35,786,213 to the nearest million. _____

10. Round off .64347894 to the nearest thousandth. _____

11. 647 × .45 = _____

12. Write MCCCXLII in Arabic numbers. _____

    Write 2,863 in Roman numerals. _____

13. 18.441 ÷ .27 = _____

Review Test Progress Graph

After each Review Test is corrected, make a bar graph by filling in the number of questions you got right. The top line climbing up the graph is the number of questions on each test, so if you touch the line, you got one hundred percent correct. The lower line climbing up the graph indicates eighty percent correct or the mastery level which you should reach. During the year, you'll be able to see your progress in math.

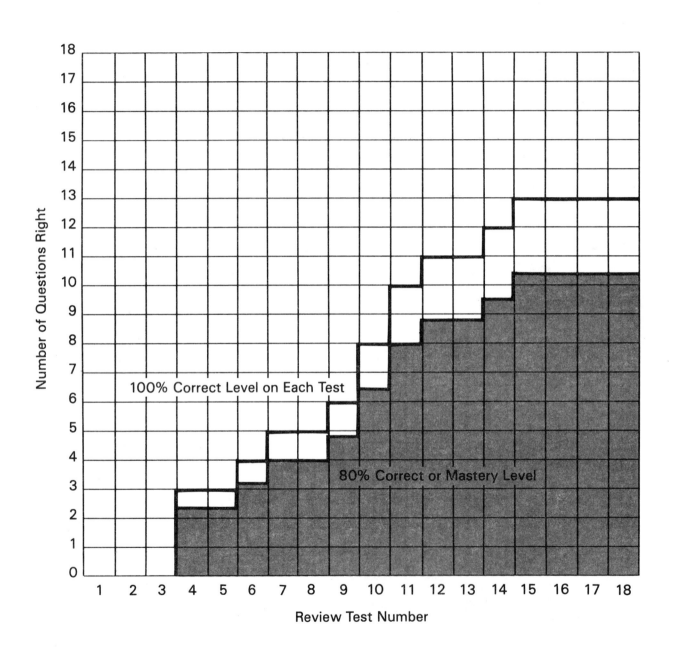

Number of Questions Right

100% Correct Level on Each Test

80% Correct or Mastery Level

Review Test Number